# Contents

# NUMBER Place value

**1** Four friends finish a game of Scrabble®.

I scored one hundred and six

I scored eighty-nine

I scored one hundred and twenty

I scored ninety-three

Olivia    Daniel    Emily    Jerzy

**a** Who won the game?

_____

1 mark

**b** Write the scores in figures, starting with the largest.

_____ , _____ , _____ , _____

2 marks

**2 a** What number is 100 less than 399?

_____

1 mark

**b** What number is 1 less than 3.1?

_____

1 mark

**3** Here are 5 number cards.  6  9  4  5  1

Jade picks three cards and makes this number.  4  9  5

Carlos picks three cards and makes this number.  6  1  5

**a** Make a larger number than 495 with Jade's three cards.

_____

1 mark

**b** Make a smaller odd number than 615 with Carlos' three cards.

_____

1 mark

**c** Using any three of the cards make an even number between 495 and 615.

_____

1 mark

4

**4** The attendance at a football game was 8007.

  **a** Write the number 8007 in words.

  _____

  **b** The capacity of the ground is 10 000. How many more fans could have attended?

  _____

**5** Write down the value of the number halfway between the numbers shown

  **a**

    15            □         23

  **b**

    1.1            □        1.4

**6** A three-digit number is made from three number cards  | 3 | 7 | 2 |

  when the digits are reversed the number becomes  | 2 | 7 | 3 |

  **a** What is the difference between 372 and 273?

    _____

  **b** Which digit represents the same value in each number?

    _____

**7** Fill in the missing numbers on the number line.

  | 6.6 | 6.7 | □ | □ | □ | □ |

**levels 3-4**

**1** Write in the missing numbers.

a  $\boxed{37}$ + $\boxed{26}$ = $\boxed{\phantom{00}}$       **1 mark**

b  $\boxed{37}$ – $\boxed{\phantom{00}}$ = $\boxed{16}$     **1 mark**

**2** Find the answer to the following.

a  634 + 179

_____      **1 mark**

b  518 – 329

_____     **1 mark**

**3** Work out the following.

a  Add 178 to half of 248.

_____      **2 marks**

b  Add 145 to 325, then subtract 275.

_____      **2 marks**

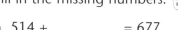

**4** Fill in the missing numbers.

a  514 + _____ = 677     b  873 – _____ = 576

c  _____ – 226 = 514     d  _____ + 371 = 482      **4 marks**

**5** Each side of the triangle adds up to the same number.
Use these numbers to complete the triangle.

$\boxed{2}$  $\boxed{3}$  $\boxed{6}$

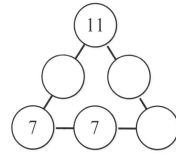

**2 marks**

**6 a** Salma did a sponsored swim.
She swam 9 lengths and collected
35 pence for every length.
How much did she collect altogether?
Give your answer in pounds.

_____

1 mark

**b** Ingrid also did a sponsored swim.
She was sponsored 80p per length and raised a total of £19.20.
How many lengths did she swim?

_____

1 mark

**7** Fill in the missing numbers.

**a** 46 x _____ = 828          **b** 684 ÷ _____ = 36

**c** _____ x 22 = 748          **d** _____ ÷ 37 = 15

4 marks

**8** A lottery syndicate wins £225 000.
**a** There are 25 members in the syndicate who get an equal share of the winnings.
How much does each member of the syndicate receive?

_____

1 mark

**b** Ben, one of the members, decides to share £4500 of his winnings between
his 9 grandchildren. How much does each child receive?

_____

1 mark

**9** There are 8 pencils in a box. A box of pencils costs £1.44.
**a** How many pencils are there in 15 boxes?

_____

1 mark

**b** How much does each pencil cost?

_____

1 mark

**1** Work out the following.

   **a** 0.4 + 0.7 _____

   **b** 2.7 – 1.3 _____

   **c** 3.2 + 4.97 _____

   **d** 36.34 – 16.5 _____

**2** **a** Johannes pays £1.25 for a bus ticket to work and £1.10 for a bus ticket on the way home from work.
   How much does he pay altogether?

   _____

   **b** How much would he save if he bought a day pass for £1.80?

   _____

**3** Here are 5 cards.  | 3 | 0 | . | 8 | 5 |

   **a** Make a number between 3 and 4 with three of the cards.  ☐ ☐ ☐

   **b** Make a number less than 0.5 with three of the cards.  ☐ ☐ ☐

**4** Put the following decimals in order with the smallest first.
   1.23,   3.21,   2.3,   0.1

   _____ , _____ , _____ , _____

**5 a** Adam buys a burger, fries and a drink.
How much does he pay?

£1.85  95p  65p

_____

1 mark

**b** A 'Meal Deal' gives a burger, fries and a drink for £2.95.
How much would Adam save with a 'Meal Deal'?

_____

1 mark

**6** The map shows three towns A, B and C and the distances between them.

23.8 km

16.5 km

35.2 km

**a** Cameron drives from A to B and then to C.

How far does he travel altogether? _____

1 mark

**b** How much further does he travel than the direct route from A to C?

_____

1 mark

**7** Put the signs < (less than), > (greater than) or = (equals) between these statements to make them true. The first is done for you.

**a** 2.3 + 1.7 > 6.5 – 3.1       **b** 3.5 – 0.8 _____ 2.6 + 0.2

**c** 1.98 + 3.1 _____ 2.98 + 2.1   **d** 6 – 4.7 _____ 2 + 0.3

3 marks

**8** Write a number to complete these calculations. The first is done for you.

**a** 6.2 + 0.8 = 4.2 + 2.8       **b** 5.6 – 2.8 = 7.6 – _____

**c** 1.2 + 6.7 = 5.2 + _____   **d** 8 – 1.6 = 7 – _____

3 marks

# NUMBER

# Long multiplication and division

**1** Work out the following.

   **a** 27 x 32

   _____    **2 marks**

   **b** 36 x 217

   _____    **2 marks**

   **c** 952 ÷ 28

   _____    **2 marks**

   **d** 994 ÷ 14

   _____    **2 marks**

**2 a** Eggs are delivered in trays of 48.
How many eggs will be in 17 trays?

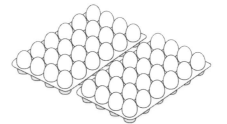

   _____    **2 marks**

   **b** A restaurant orders 1000 eggs.

     **i** How many full trays will they need?    _____    **2 marks**

     **ii** How many eggs will be in the last tray?    _____    **2 marks**

**3** One bus carries 52 passengers.

   **a** How many passengers could be
carried on 23 buses?

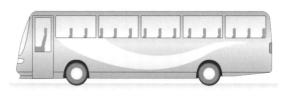

   _____    **2 marks**

   **b** A school is taking 950 students to a theme park at the end of term.
How many buses will they need to hire?

   _____    **2 marks**

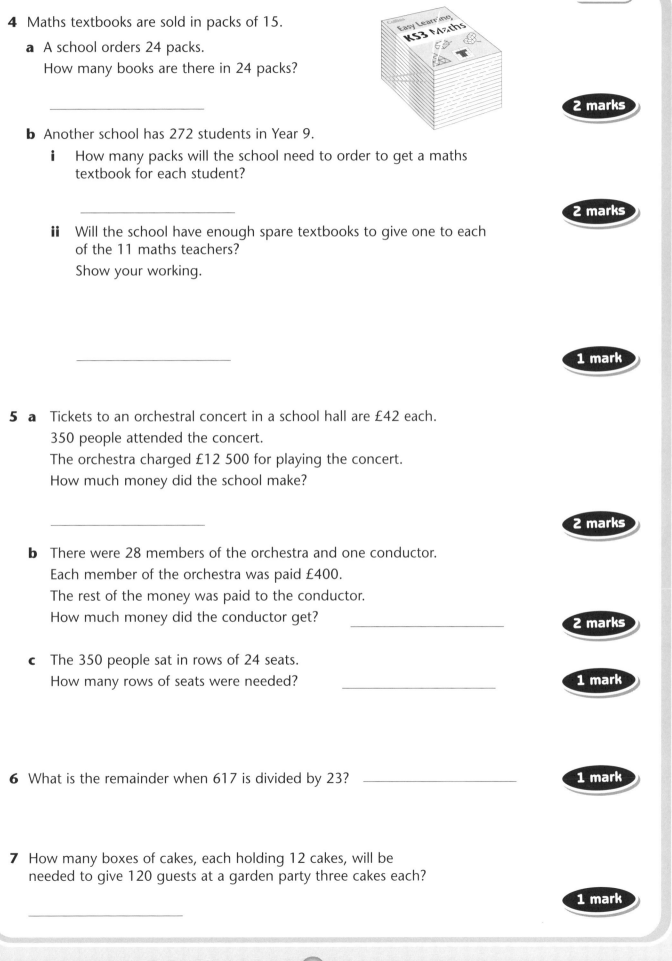

**4** Maths textbooks are sold in packs of 15.

    **a** A school orders 24 packs.

       How many books are there in 24 packs?

       _____

       **2 marks**

    **b** Another school has 272 students in Year 9.

       **i** How many packs will the school need to order to get a maths
          textbook for each student?

          _____

       **2 marks**

       **ii** Will the school have enough spare textbooks to give one to each
          of the 11 maths teachers?

          Show your working.

          _____

       **1 mark**

**5**  **a** Tickets to an orchestral concert in a school hall are £42 each.
      350 people attended the concert.
      The orchestra charged £12 500 for playing the concert.
      How much money did the school make?

      _____

      **2 marks**

    **b** There were 28 members of the orchestra and one conductor.
      Each member of the orchestra was paid £400.
      The rest of the money was paid to the conductor.
      How much money did the conductor get?   _____   **2 marks**

    **c** The 350 people sat in rows of 24 seats.
      How many rows of seats were needed?   _____   **1 mark**

**6** What is the remainder when 617 is divided by 23?   _____   **1 mark**

**7** How many boxes of cakes, each holding 12 cakes, will be
   needed to give 120 guests at a garden party three cakes each?

   **1 mark**

_____

# Rounding and approximation

levels 3-4

**1** Round off the number 367 to

**a** the nearest 10 ____________________ 1 mark

**b** the nearest 100 ____________________ 1 mark

**2** Round off the number 4562 to

**a** the nearest 10 ____________________ 1 mark

**b** the nearest 100 ____________________ 1 mark

**c** the nearest 1000 ____________________ 1 mark

**3** Round off the number 5.687 to

**a** 1 decimal place ____________________ 1 mark

**b** 2 decimal places ____________________ 1 mark

**4** Round off the following numbers to 1 significant figure.

**a** 2762 ____________________ 1 mark

**b** 5.92 ____________________ 1 mark

**c** 183 ____________________ 1 mark

**d** 0.079 ____________________ 1 mark

**5** The picture shows a man standing by a bus.

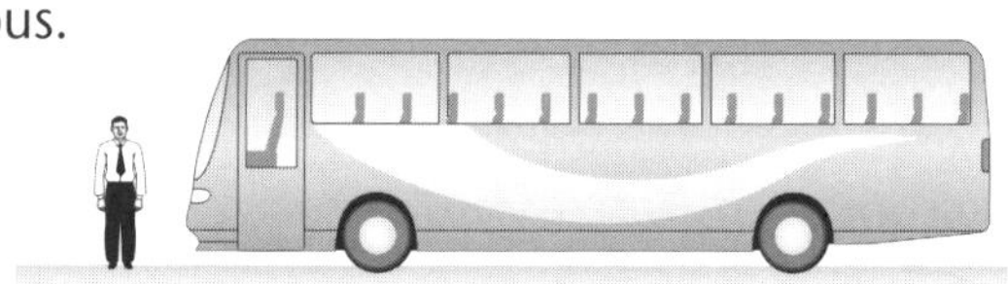

**a** Estimate the height of the bus.

____________________ 1 mark

**b** Estimate the length of the bus.

____________________ 1 mark

**6** By rounding these numbers to 1 significant figure, estimate answers
to these calculations.

   **a** 49.6 x 11.3 _____

   **b** 187 ÷ 38.6 _____

**7** By rounding these numbers to 1 significant figure, estimate answers
to these calculations.

   **a** $\dfrac{198 + 421}{23 + 12}$    _____

   **b** $\dfrac{32.7 \times 59.8}{19.3}$    _____

**8** A jar of sweets is labelled 'Contains 100 sweets (to the nearest 10)'.

   **a** What is the least number of sweets in the jar? _____

   **b** What is the greatest possible number of sweets in the jar?

   _____

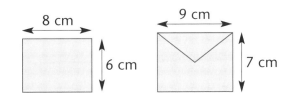

**9** Class 9R are making Christmas cards.
The cards are 6 cm by 8 cm, each side being
measured to the nearest cm.
Envelopes are made to a size of 9 cm by 7 cm.

   **a** Explain why cards cannot be any wider than $8\frac{1}{2}$ cm.

   _____

   **b** What is the smallest height the envelopes could be?

   _____ 1 mark

   **c** Explain why the cards will fit into the envelopes.

   _____ 1 mark

# NUMBER

# Multiplying and dividing decimals

**1** Look at these five cards.      0

    **a** Deepak picks two cards and makes the number 25.

       Which extra card should he pick to make his number 10 times bigger?

    _____

                              **1 mark**

    **b** Samuel picks three cards and makes the number 5.6

       Show the three cards Samuel needs to make a number that is
       100 times bigger than 5.6

    [ ] [ ] [ ]

                              **1 mark**

**2** The diagram shows how to change metres into millimetres.

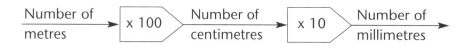

| Number of metres | → | x 100 | Number of centimetres | → | x 10 | Number of millimetres | → |

    **a** Change 3.4 metres into millimetres.

    _____

                              **1 mark**

    **b** Change 74 millimetres into metres.

                              **1 mark**

    _____

**3** Fill in the missing numbers.

    **a** $5 \div 10 =$ _____         **b** _____ $\times 100 = 23$

    **c** $0.6 \div 100 =$ _____      **d** $0.6 \times$ _____ $= 60$    **4 marks**

**4** Paul spends £17.10 each week on train fares.

    **a** How much would he spend on train fares on 4 weeks?

                              **1 mark**

    _____

    **b** How much would he save with a monthly pass that costs £56.50?

                              **1 mark**

    _____

**5** Complete this tuck shop order.

100 Mars bars at £0.37 each      £ _____

100 Twix bars at £0.35 each      £ _____

50 Mini fudge bars at £0.18 each      £ _____

             Total    £ _____

**4 marks**

**6** Maria bought 3 CDs and 5 DVDs.
How much does she pay altogether?

£15.95

£8.99

_____

**2 marks**

**7** Jamal buys 5 new tyres for his car.
The total bill is £325.
How much was each tyre?

_____

**1 mark**

**8** Work out the following.

   **a** 4.6 x 7 = _____        **b** 35.4 ÷ 6 = _____

   **c** 8 x 5.2 = _____        **d** 58.1 ÷ 7 = _____

**4 marks**

**9** Six people buy a meal in a restaurant and
the bill comes to £256.80.

If they share the cost equally how much
does each person pay?

_____

**1 mark**

# NUMBER  Negative numbers

**1** The number line shows the surface temperature of the planets.

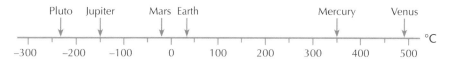

**a** Which planet has a temperature of about −20 °C?

_____

**1 mark**

**b** Which planet has a temperature of about 350 °C?

_____

**1 mark**

**c** What is the approximate difference in temperature between the coldest and the warmest planet?

_____

**1 mark**

**2** Look at this list of numbers.

−7, −6, −2, −1, 0, 2, 4, 8

**a** What is the total of all eight numbers?

_____

**1 mark**

**b** Choose three different numbers that have the lowest total.

_____

**1 mark**

**c** Choose two numbers so that the product is as low as possible.

_____

**1 mark**

**3** The diagram shows how to change °C into °F.

**a** Change 20 °C into °F. _____

**1 mark**

**b** Change −40 °C into °F. _____

**1 mark**

**c** Change −4 °F into °C. _____

**1 mark**

**4** Using = (equals), < (less than) or > (greater than), put the correct sign between each number sentence. The first one has been done for you.

**a** 5 – 6 < 6 – 5

**b** –9 _____ –3

**c** +7 – –8 _____ +8 – –7

**d** 4 x –2 _____ –4 x 2

**3 marks**

**5** Work out the following.

**a** –8 + 3 – 6 _____

**b** –3 x –2 + 5 _____

**c** –32 ÷ + 8 _____

**d** (–4 – 3) x –6 _____

**4 marks**

**6** Fill in two **negative** numbers to make the following true.

**a** ☐ + ☐ = –5

**2 marks**

**b** ☐ – ☐ = –5

**2 marks**

**7** Write the missing numbers on the number lines.

**a**
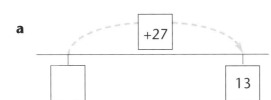

**b**
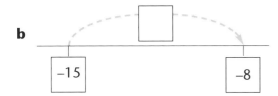

**c**
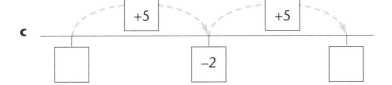

**4 marks**

17

# Adding and subtracting fractions

**1** The table shows some fractions of amounts of money.

|  | £8 | £10 | £22 |
|---|---|---|---|
| $\frac{1}{2}$ | £4.00 | £5.00 | £11.00 |
| $\frac{1}{4}$ | £2.00 | £2.50 | £5.50 |
| $\frac{1}{8}$ | £1.00 | £1.25 | £2.75 |

Use the table to work out the missing numbers.

**a** $\frac{3}{8}$ of £22 = _____

**b** £7.50 = _____ of £10

**c** £5 = $\frac{5}{8}$ of

**d** £4 = $\frac{1}{8}$ of

**2** Work out the missing numbers or fractions.

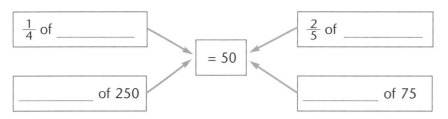

$\frac{1}{4}$ of _____

_____ of 250

= 50

$\frac{2}{5}$ of _____

_____ of 75

**3** Work out the missing numbers.

**a** $\frac{4}{12} = \frac{\square}{3}$

**b** $\frac{5}{7} = \frac{15}{\square}$

**2 marks**

**4 a** How many sixths are there in $2\frac{5}{6}$? _____

**1 mark**

**b** How many sixths are in $1\frac{2}{3}$? _____

**1 mark**

**5** Work out the following.

**a** $\frac{1}{3} + \frac{2}{5}$ _____ **2 marks**

**b** $\frac{3}{5} - \frac{1}{4}$ _____ **2 marks**

**6** Work out the following.

**a** $2\frac{1}{4} + 3\frac{1}{5}$ _____ **2 marks**

**b** $2\frac{3}{4} - 1\frac{1}{3}$ _____ **2 marks**

**7** The diagram shows a grey rectangle that is 8 cm by 6 cm. Two black squares, one 4 cm by 4 cm and the other 2 cm by 2 cm, are drawn inside it.

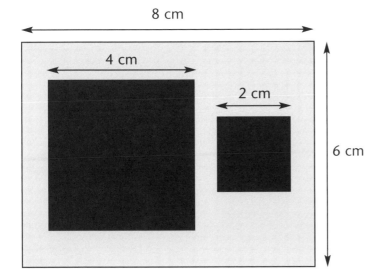

**a** What fraction of the rectangle is shaded black?

_____ **2 marks**

**b** What fraction of the rectangle is shaded grey?

_____ **2 marks**

# NUMBER

# Multiplying and dividing fractions

**1** What is the highest common factor of 12 and 42?
Tick the correct answer.

☐ 12    ☐ 42    ☐ 2    ☐ 6

**1 mark**

**2** What is the mixed number $3\frac{2}{3}$, when written as a top-heavy fraction?
Tick the correct answer.

☐ $\frac{32}{3}$    ☐ $\frac{11}{3}$    ☐ $\frac{12}{3}$    ☐ 0.66

**1 mark**

**3** The fraction of red balls placed in a bag is $\frac{1}{3}$. Half of these red balls are taken out.
What fraction of the red balls is in the bag now?
Tick the correct answer.

☐ $\frac{1}{3}$    ☐ $\frac{1}{5}$    ☐ $\frac{1}{6}$    ☐ $\frac{1}{12}$

**1 mark**

**4** Some examples of multiplying fractions are shown.

$\frac{2}{3} \times \frac{4}{5} = \frac{8}{15}$ , $\frac{1}{4} \times \frac{3}{7} = \frac{3}{28}$ , $\frac{3}{5} \times \frac{4}{11} = \frac{12}{55}$

Which of the following is the answer to $\frac{a}{b} \times \frac{c}{d}$ ?
Tick the correct answer.

☐ $\frac{a}{cbd}$    ☐ $\frac{ac}{bd}$    ☐ $\frac{ad}{cb}$    ☐ $\frac{ab}{cd}$

**1 mark**

**5** What is $\frac{3}{4} \times \frac{1}{6}$ in its simplest form? _____

**1 mark**

**6** Work out $\frac{1}{8} \div \frac{5}{6}$ and give the answer in its simplest form.

_____

**1 mark**

20

**7** How many $\frac{1}{5}$ are in $2\frac{2}{5}$ ? _____

**8** The table shows some fractions of different weights.

|  | 7.5 kg | 12 kg | 21 kg |
|---|---|---|---|
| $\frac{1}{2}$ | 3.75 kg | 6 kg | 10.5 kg |
| $\frac{1}{3}$ | 2.5 kg | 4 kg | 7 kg |
| $\frac{1}{6}$ | 1.25 kg | 2 kg | 3.5 kg |

Use the table to work out the missing numbers.

**a** $\frac{2}{3}$ x 28.5 kg = _____

**b** 5.5 kg = _____ x 33 kg

**c** 6.5 kg = $\frac{1}{3}$ x _____

**d** 6.75 kg = $\frac{1}{6}$ x _____

**9** Work out the following.

**a** $\frac{1}{9}$ x $\frac{3}{5}$ _____

**b** $\frac{3}{10}$ ÷ $\frac{6}{25}$ _____

**10** Work out the following.

**a** $2\frac{1}{4}$ x $1\frac{1}{5}$ _____

**b** $2\frac{3}{4}$ ÷ $4\frac{1}{8}$ _____

# NUMBER

# Equivalent fractions, percentages and decimals

**1** Fill in the equivalent fractions, percentages and decimals as appropriate. The first line has been done for you.

|   | Fraction | Percentage | Decimal |
|---|---|---|---|
| a | $\frac{1}{4}$ | 25% | 0.25 |
| b | $\frac{3}{5}$ |  |  |
| c |  | 75% |  |
| d |  |  | 0.9 |

**6 marks**

**2 a** Complete these sentences.

**i** _____ **out of 10** is the same as 60%.

**1 mark**

**ii** **24 out of 50** is the same as _____%.

**1 mark**

**b** Complete these sentences using different pairs of numbers.

**i** _____ out of _____ is the same as 20%.

**1 mark**

**ii** _____ out of _____ is the same as 20%.

**1 mark**

**3** About 40% of this shape is shaded grey.

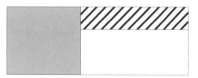

**a** Approximately what percentage is striped? _____

**1 mark**

**b** Approximately what percentage is white? _____

**1 mark**

**4** Look at the diagram.

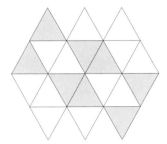

   **a** What fraction is shaded? _____

                                                          `1 mark`

   **b** What percentage is shaded? _____

                                                          `1 mark`

**5** The pie charts show the types of houses in two housing estates.

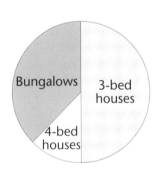

          **Estate A**                **Estate B**

   **a** What percentage of the houses on estate A are 4-bed houses? _____   `1 mark`

   **b** What fraction of the houses on estate B are bungalows? _____   `1 mark`

   **c** Tick the statement that is true.

      ☐ There are more bungalows on estate A than B.

      ☐ There are fewer bungalows on estate A than B.

      ☐ There are equal numbers of bungalows on estate A and B.

      ☐ You cannot tell how many bungalows are on each estate.   `1 mark`

**1** Alex asked 50 children what their favourite lunch was.

| Lunch | Boys | Girls |
|---|---|---|
| Pizza | 4 | 3 |
| Burgers | 6 | 6 |
| Fish cakes | 2 | 3 |
| Sausages | 7 | 6 |
| Salad | 1 | 12 |
| Total | 20 | 30 |

**a** What percentage of the children surveyed preferred pizza?

_____

1 mark

**b** Which lunch did 10% of the boys prefer?   _____

1 mark

**c** Which lunch did 40% of the girls prefer?   _____

1 mark

**d** Alex said, 'My survey shows that burgers are just as popular with girls as with boys'. Explain why Alex is wrong.

_____

_____

1 mark

**e** Which lunch is equally popular with boys and girls?   _____

1 mark

**2** A clothes shop is having a sale.
All clothes are reduced by 20%.

**a** What is the sale price of a jacket normally priced at £60?

_____

1 mark

**b** What is the sale price of a shirt normally priced at £32?

_____

1 mark

**c** On the last day of the sale, the **sale price** is reduced by a further 10%.
Which of the following is the last day price of a pair of boots normally priced at £100? Tick the correct answer.

☐ £80   ☐ £70   ☐ £72   ☐ £90

1 mark

**3** The table shows the 2005 population of each of the world's continents.

| Continent | Population (in millions) |
|---|---|
| Australasia | 33 |
| Africa | 841 |
| Asia | 3825 |
| Europe | 735 |
| North America | 492 |
| South America | 379 |
| **World total** | 6305 |

**a** Which continent had about 6% of the world's population in 2005?

_____

**1 mark**

**b** In 2005, what percentage of the world's population was living in Africa?

_____

**2 marks**

**4** The pie chart shows how a farmer uses his land.
The angle for fallow land is 45°.

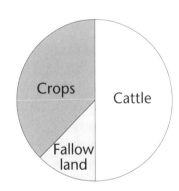

**a** What percentage of the farm is fallow land?

_____

**1 mark**

**b** 330 acres are used for crops. What is the
total acreage of the farm?

_____

**2 marks**

**c** Next year the farmer plans to decrease the acreage for cattle
by $33\frac{1}{3}$ % and increase the amount for crops by $33\frac{1}{3}$ %.
Tick the statement that is true.

☐  The amount of fallow land will stay the same.

☐  The amount of fallow land will increase.

☐  The amount of fallow land will decrease.

☐  You cannot tell how the amount of fallow land will change.

**1 mark**

# NUMBER    Ratio

**1**  **a**  Write the ratio 6 : 9 in its simplest form. _____

**1 mark**

   **b**  Write the ratio 15 : 25 in its simplest form. _____

**1 mark**

**2**  The ratio of two packets of cornflakes is 3 : 4. Find the mass of the larger packet.

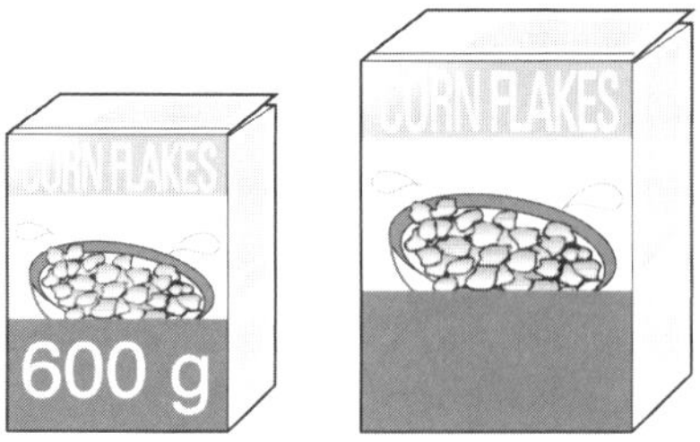

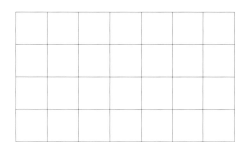

600 g

**2 marks**

_____

**3**  Shade the diagram so that the ratio of shaded squares to unshaded squares is 1 : 3

**1 mark**

**4**  **a**  Divide £90 in the ratio 1 : 4  _____

**2 marks**

   **b**  Divide 150 kg in the ratio 2 : 3  _____

**2 marks**

**5**  A drink is made from cranberry juice and lemonade in the ratio 2 : 7

   **a**  How much lemonade is needed if 50 ml of cranberry juice is used?

**2 marks**

   _____

   **b**  How much cranberry juice is in 450 ml of the drink?

**2 marks**

   _____

**6** The diagram shows a grey rectangle
8 cm by 6 cm with a black square
3 cm by 3 cm drawn inside it.

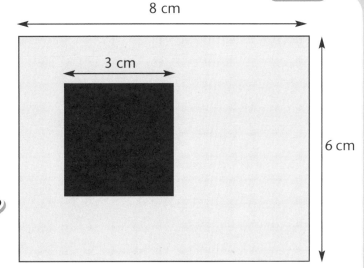

8 cm

3 cm

6 cm

**a** Calculate the ratio of the perimeter of
the rectangle to the perimeter of the
square. Give your answer in its
simplest form.

_____  **2 marks**

**b** Calculate the ratio
grey area : black area

Give your answer in its simplest form.

_____  **2 marks**

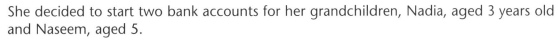

**7** Fatima won £146 on the lottery.
She decided to start two bank accounts for her grandchildren, Nadia, aged 3 years old
and Naseem, aged 5.
She shared the money between the children in the ratio of their ages.

**a** How much did each child get in the bank? _____  **2 marks**

**b** The following year she won another £146 and did the same thing with the money.

How much would each child have in the bank in total now?

_____  **2 marks**

**8** A fizzy drink is sold in two sizes. The small bottle
costs 35p and the larger bottle costs 60p.

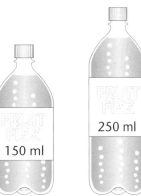

250 ml

150 ml

**a** Write down the ratio of the sizes of the bottles in
its simplest form. _____  **1 mark**

**b** Write down the ratio of the costs of the bottles in
its simplest form. _____  **1 mark**

**c** Which size is the best value for money?

Explain your answer. _____  **2 marks**

**Number patterns**

**1** What is the next term in this sequence: 4, 9, 14, 19, 24, ... ? _____ **1 mark**

**2** What is the term-to-term rule for this sequence?

7, 11, 15, 19, 23, ...

Tick the correct answer.

☐ add 2 each time          ☐ add 3 each time

☐ add 4 each time          ☐ add 5 each time          **1 mark**

**3** The term-to-term rule for a sequence is 'add one more each time'.
Which of the following sequences obey this rule?
Tick the correct answer. (There may be more than one.)

☐ 1, 3, 6, 10, 15, ...

☐ 1, 3, 6, 9, 12, ...

☐ 5, 7, 10, 14, 19, ...

☐ 100, 99, 97, 94, 90, ...          **1 mark**

**4** What is the next number in this sequence: 10, 7, 4, 1, –2, ... ? _____ **1 mark**

**5** A sequence has the term-to-term rule 'multiply by 2 and add 1'.
Which of these series of three terms could be in the sequence?
Tick the correct answer. (There may be more than one.)

☐ 1, 3, 5, ...

☐ 2, 5, 11, ...

☐ 10, 21, 63, ...

☐ –3, –5, –9, ...          **1 mark**

**6** The *n*th term of a sequence is 2*n* – 1.

Write down the first three terms of the sequence. _____

**7** Look at this series of patterns.

   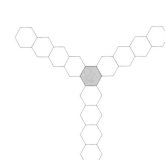

**Pattern 1**

**Pattern 2**

**Pattern 3**

**Pattern 4**

  **a**  How many grey hexagons will there be in Pattern 6?

_____

  **b**  What is the *n*th term of the sequence for the number of white hexagons?

_____

**8** Look at this series of patterns.

   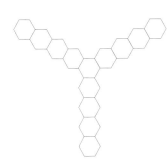

**Pattern 1**

**Pattern 2**

**Pattern 3**

**Pattern 4**

What is the *n*th term of the number of hexagons in this sequence?

_____

**9** What is the missing term in this sequence?

3, 4, ... , 12, 19, 28, 39, 52             _____

**10** What is the *n*th term in this sequence?

8, 12, 16, 20, 24, ...             _____

# Multiples, factors, square numbers and primes

**1** What are the first 3 multiples of 7? _____ , _____ , _____

**1 mark**

**2** What is the $n$th term of the series: 1, 4, 9, 16, 25, ... ? _____

**1 mark**

**3** Which of these statements are true and which are false?
Tick the correct box for each statement.

|  | True | False |
|---|---|---|
| If $x^2 = 64$, then $x$ must equal 8. | ☐ | ☐ |
| All numbers have an even number of factors. | ☐ | ☐ |
| 81 is a square number. | ☐ | ☐ |
| 1 is a factor of all numbers. | ☐ | ☐ |
| Numbers with only 2 factors are called prime numbers. | ☐ | ☐ |
| All prime numbers are odd. | ☐ | ☐ |

**6 marks**

**4** Write down the factors of 24. _____

**2 marks**

**5** What is the highest common factor of 24 and 64? _____

**1 mark**

**6** What is the lowest common multiple of 9 and 12? _____

**1 mark**

**7** Which of the following is both a square number and a triangle number?
Tick the correct answer.

☐ 4    ☐ 9    ☐ 25    ☐ 36

**1 mark**

**8** Write down a square number between 101 and 149. _____

**9** Here are 10 number cards. ⎡1⎤ ⎡2⎤ ⎡3⎤ ⎡4⎤ ⎡5⎤ ⎡6⎤ ⎡7⎤ ⎡8⎤ ⎡9⎤ ⎡10⎤

From the cards, write down

**a** the square numbers _____

**b** the prime numbers _____

**c** the factors of 10 _____

**10** Circle A contains the first ten multiples of 2.
Circle B contains the first seven multiples of 3.

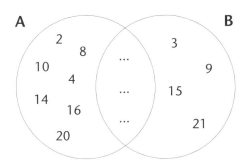

Write down the missing numbers
from the overlap.

_____
_____
_____

**11** Circle A contains the factors of 20.
Circle B contains the factors of 36.

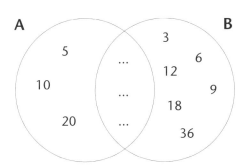

Write down the missing numbers
from the overlap.

_____
_____
_____

# Basic algebra

**1** Simplify $2a \times 4a$ _____

*1 mark*

**2** Simplify $6a + 7 - 4a + 8$ _____

*1 mark*

**3** If $a = 2$, what is the value of $3a + 7$? _____

*1 mark*

**4** Simplify $2a + 5a - 4a$ _____

*1 mark*

**5** Which of the following are equivalent to the algebraic expression $3n + 4m$?
Tick the correct answer. (There may be more than one.)

☐ $3 + n + 4 + m$  ☐ $6n + 5m - m - 3n$

☐ $12nm$  ☐ $2m + 2m + 2n + n$

*1 mark*

**6** If $a = 3$, $b = 4$ and $c = 5$ which of the following expressions are equal to 27?
Tick the correct answer. (There may be more than one.)

☐ $a(b + c)$  ☐ $a^2 + b^2$

☐ $ab + ac$  ☐ $c^2 + 2$

*1 mark*

**7** Which of the following are equivalent to the algebraic expression $2n$?
Tick the correct answer. (There may be more than one.)

☐ $n \times 2$  ☐ $n^2$

☐ $\sqrt{4n}$  ☐ $12n \div 6$

*1 mark*

**8** Simplify the following expressions.

   **a** $5a + 6b - 2a - b$ _____

   **b** $3a \times 5a$ _____

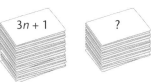

**9** Alyssa has a pile of cards.
   The total number of cards is $4n + 8$.

   **a** Alyssa puts the cards into 2 piles.
   The number of cards in one pile is $3n + 1$.
   How many cards are in the other pile?

   _____

   **b** Alyssa puts the cards into 4 equal piles.

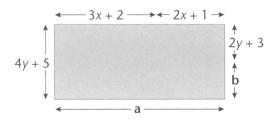

   How many cards are in each pile?

   _____

   **c** Alyssa counts the cards and finds she has 32 in total.
   What is the value of $n$?

   _____

**10** Look at the rectangle. Write down expressions for the lengths marked **a** and **b**.

   **a** = _____

   **b** = _____

# ALGEBRA    Formulae

**1** The charge for using a gymnasium is

£5 per visit
plus 50p per hour

**a** How much will it cost to use the gym for 2 hours?

_____

`1 mark`

**b** If someone paid £7, how many hours did they use the gym for?

_____

`1 mark`

**2** Which of the following could be a formula that changes 3 into 15.
Tick the correct answer. (There may be more than one.)

☐ add 12

☐ multiply by 5

☐ subtract 12

☐ multiply by 6 and subtract 3

`1 mark`

**3** A garden centre uses this formula to work out the cost of a bay tree.

**£7 x height of tree in feet plus £10**

**a** How much will a bay tree that is 4 feet high cost?

_____

`1 mark`

**b** A bay tree is priced at £27.50. How tall is it?

_____

`1 mark`

**4** The flow diagram shows a formula.

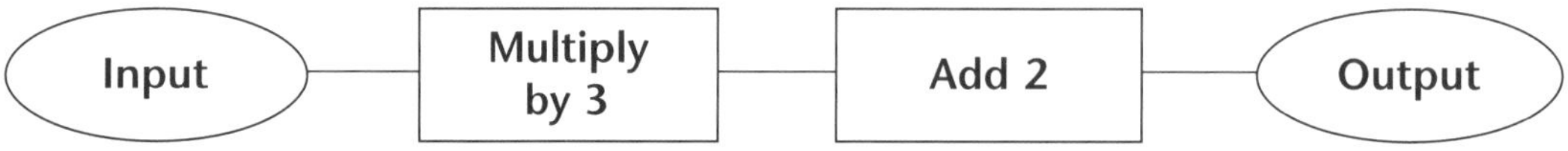

Input — Multiply by 3 — Add 2 — Output

Which of the following pairs of inputs and outputs work for this formula?
Tick the correct answer. (There may be more than one.)

☐ input 3, output 15

☐ input 5, output 17

☐ input 1, output 5

☐ input −2, output −8

`1 mark`

**5** Greg is thinking of a number.

I think of a number.
I double it and add 7.
The answer is 12.

What is the number?

_____

**6**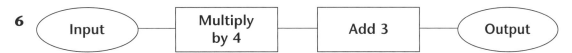

( Input ) — | Multiply by 4 | — | Add 3 | — ( Output )

**a** What is the output for this flow diagram if the input is 5? _____

**b** What is the input for this flow diagram if the output is 5? _____

**7**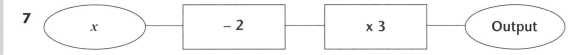

( $x$ ) — | – 2 | — | x 3 | — ( Output )

What formula will be the output from this flow diagram?

_____

**8** In a sale the prices are reduced by 20%.
This flow diagram shows how to work out the sale price.

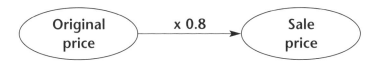

( Original price ) —— x 0.8 —→ ( Sale price )

**a** What is the sale price of an item with an original price of £20?

_____

**b** What is the original price of an item with a sale price of £32?

_____

**1** What are the coordinates of

A ( _____ , _____ )

B ( _____ , _____ )

C ( _____ , _____ )

D ( _____ , _____ )

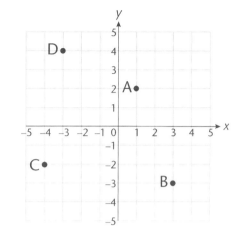

**4 marks**

**2** What relationship do the points marked on this grid obey?

Tick the correct answer.

☐ $y + x = -3$

☐ $y = x - 3$

☐ $y = x - 5$

☐ $x + y = 3$

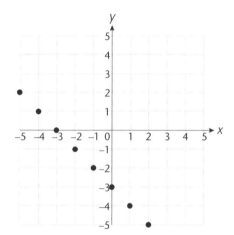

**1 mark**

**3 a** What is the midpoint of AB?

_____

**1 mark**

  **b** The point C is on the same horizontal line as A and the same vertical line as B. What are the coordinates of C?

_____

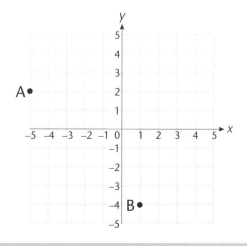

**1 mark**

4 Some points are plotted that obey the relationship $y - x = 5$.
Which of the following coordinates obey the relationship?
Tick the correct answer. (There may be more than one.)

☐ (7, 2)   ☐ (–1, 4)   ☐ (5, 0)   ☐ $(2\frac{1}{2}, 7\frac{1}{2})$

**1 mark**

5 a A, B and C are three corners of a parallelogram. What are the coordinates of the fourth corner?

_____

**1 mark**

b X, Y and Z are three corners of a rectangle.
What are the coordinates of the other corner?

_____

**1 mark**

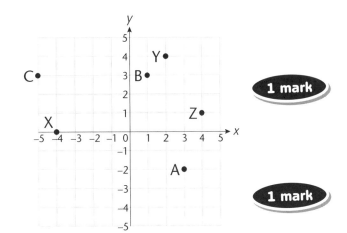

6 Some rectangular tiles are placed on a coordinate grid.

On the first tile, the corner marked with a square has the coordinate (2, 2) and the corner marked with a triangle has the coordinate (0, 1).

a What are the coordinates of the corner with a square on tile 6?

_____

**1 mark**

b What are the coordinates of the corner with a triangle on tile 7?

_____

**1 mark**

c What are the coordinates of the corner with a square on tile 20?

_____

**1 mark**

d What are the coordinates of the corner with a triangle on tile 21?

_____

**1 mark**

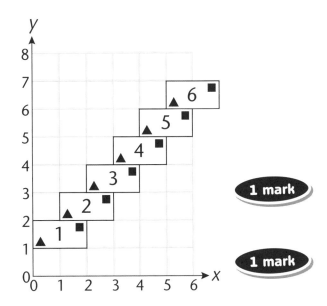

**Drawing graphs**

**1** What are the equations of the graphs
**a, b, c, d**?

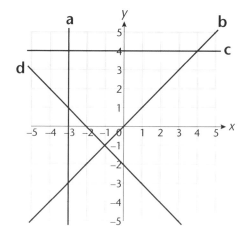

a _____

b _____

c _____

d _____

**4 marks**

**2** A is the point (2, 5). B is the point (–3, 5).

Which of the following is the graph of the straight line through A and B?

☐ $y = 2x + 1$     ☐ $y = x + 3$     ☐ $y = 5$     ☐ $y = x + 8$

**1 mark**

**3** The equation of a line is $y + x = 8$.

Which of the following points could lie on the line?

Tick the correct answer. (There could be more than one.)

☐ (–2, –6)     ☐ (0, 8)     ☐ (–2, 10)     ☐ (10, –2)

**1 mark**

**4** At what point do the lines $y = 3$ and $x = 2$ intersect? _____

**1 mark**

**5** Which of these lines passes through the point (–3, 5)?

Tick the correct answer. (There could be more than one.)

☐ $x + y = 8$          ☐ $y = 5$

☐ $x + y = 2$          ☐ $x = –3$

**1 mark**

**6** What are the equations of the graphs
**a, b, c, d**?

**a** _____

**b** _____

**c** _____

**d** _____

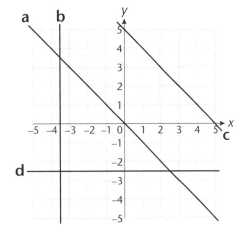

**7** A, B and C are three corners of a triangle.

   **a** What is the equation of the line

     **i** AB _____

     **ii** BC _____

     **iii** AC _____

   **b** What is the area of the triangle ABC?

     _____

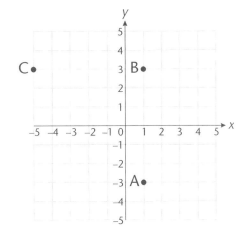

**8** Draw the following lines on the grid.

   **a** $y = 1$

   **b** $x = 2$

   **c** $x + y = 5$

   **d** What is the area of the triangle formed
     by the three lines?

     _____

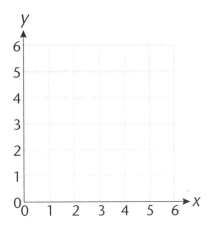

**Linear graphs**

**1** The equations of four graphs are

$y = 2x + 1$    $y = 2x - 3$    $y = 3x - 2$    $y = 4x + 1$

**a** Which two graphs are parallel?

_____

1 mark

**b** Which two lines pass through the same point on the $y$-axis?

_____

1 mark

**2** Match the lines on the graph with the equations.

$y = x + 3$ matches line _____

$y = 3x - 1$ matches line _____

$x + y = -1$ matches line _____

$y = -1$ matches line _____

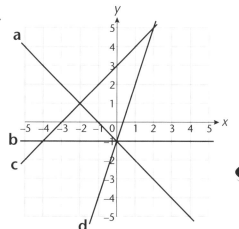

4 marks

**3** What is the equation of the line shown?

_____

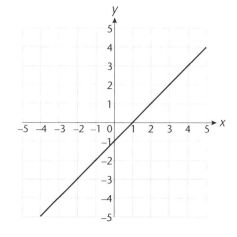

1 mark

**4** A is the point (2, 5). B is the point (–3, –5).

Which of the following is the graph of the straight line through A and B?

Tick the correct answer.

☐ $y = 2x - 1$

☐ $y = x + 3$

☐ $y = 2x + 1$

☐ $y = x - 2$

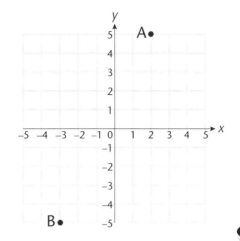

**1 mark**

**5** The equation of a line is $y = 3x - 1$.

Which of the following points could lie on the line?

Tick the correct answer. (There could be more than one.)

☐ (2, 7)        ☐ (3, 8)        ☐ (–2, –7)        ☐ (–3, 10)

**1 mark**

**6** The solid line on the graph is $y = 2x + 5$.

What is the equation of the line parallel to this line that passes through (0, –2)?

_____

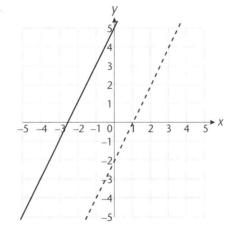

**2 marks**

**7** On the grid, draw the graphs of

**a** $y = 3x + 1$

**b** $y = 2x - 3$

**c** $y = \frac{x}{2} + 3$

**d** $y = x - 4$

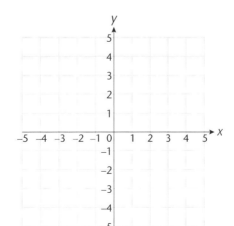

**4 marks**

**BODMAS and powers**

**1**  What is the value of $2n^2$ when $n = 10$? _____

  1 mark

**2**  What is the value of $(2n)^2$ when $n = 10$? _____

  1 mark

**3**  Put brackets in the correct place to make the following calculation true.
$6 - 2 \times 8 \div 4 - 2 = 16$

1 mark

**4**  Which of the following gives an answer of 20?
Tick the correct answer. (There may be more than one.)

☐ $2 + 8 \times 2$                    ☐ $(2 + 3)^2 - 5$

☐ $(5 - 3) \times (3 + 7)$          ☐ $4^2 \times (5 - 1)$

  1 mark

**5**  Work out $6 - (2 \times (8 \div 4) - 2)$ _____

  1 mark

**6**  Work out $5 \times (24 \div 2^2)$ _____

1 mark

**7**  Work out $72 - 5 \times 6^2 \div 3$ _____

1 mark

**8**  Work out $(4^2 \div 2) + 3 \times 4$ _____

1 mark

**9** Work out the values of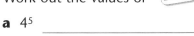

   **a** $4^5$ _____

   **1 mark**

   **b** $5^4$ _____

   **1 mark**

**10** Which is greater $2^5$ or $5^2$? _____

   **1 mark**

**11** **a** Work out

   **i** $10^2 - 8^2$ _____

   **1 mark**

   **ii** $(10 + 8)(10 - 8)$ _____

   **1 mark**

   **b** Work out the following.

   **i** $20^2 - 17^2$ _____

   **1 mark**

   **ii** $(20 + 17)(20 - 17)$ _____

   **1 mark**

   **c** Write down the answer to $90^2 - 10^2$.

   _____

   **1 mark**

**12** **a** Work out

   **i** $(4 + 2)(4 + 2)$ _____

   **1 mark**

   **ii** $4^2 + 2 \times 2 \times 4 + 2^2$ _____

   **1 mark**

   **b** Work out

   **i** $(7 - 3)(7 - 3)$ _____

   **1 mark**

   **ii** $7^2 - 2 \times 7 \times 3 + 3^2$ _____

   **1 mark**

   **c** Write down the answer to $8^2 + 2 \times 2 \times 8 + 2^2$

   _____

   **1 mark**

**1** I think of a number and add three to it. I divide the result by 5 and I get an answer of 6.
What number did I think of?

_____ **1 mark**

**2** Solve the equation $2x - 7 = 20$

_____ **1 mark**

**3** Solve these equations.

**a** $\dfrac{x - 2}{3} = 7$

_____ **1 mark**

**b** $\dfrac{x}{3} - 2 = 7$

_____ **1 mark**

**4** Solve these equations.

**a** $3x - 8 = 7$

_____ **1 mark**

**b** $\dfrac{x + 3}{8} = 3$

_____ **1 mark**

**5** Solve these equations.

**a** $\dfrac{x + 3}{5} = 6$

_____ **1 mark**

**b** $\dfrac{x}{5} + 3 = 6$

_____ **1 mark**

**c** $x + \dfrac{3}{5} = 6$

_____ **1 mark**

**d** $5x - 3 = 6$

_____ **1 mark**

**6** Solve these equations.

**a** $\dfrac{x}{6} = \dfrac{7}{4}$

_____ **1 mark**

**b** $\dfrac{x}{4} = \dfrac{9}{2}$

_____ **1 mark**

**c** $\dfrac{5}{x} = \dfrac{2}{7}$

_____ **1 mark**

**d** $\dfrac{9}{2} = \dfrac{15}{x}$

_____ **1 mark**

**7** Solve these equations.

**a** $\dfrac{x}{6} = \dfrac{7}{3}$

_____ **1 mark**

**b** $\dfrac{x + 3}{4} = \dfrac{1}{2}$

_____ **1 mark**

**8** Complete the following statements to solve

$$\dfrac{2x - 5}{2} = \dfrac{x - 4}{4}$$

$(2x - 5) \times 4 = (x - 4) \times$ _____

$8x - 20 =$ _____

$8x -$ _____ $= -8 +$ _____

$6x = 12$

$6x \div 6 = 12 \div$ _____

$x =$ _____ **2 marks**

**9** Complete the following statements to solve

$$\dfrac{4}{x + 1} = \dfrac{6}{2x - 1}$$

$4 \times (2x - 1) = 6 \times ($ _____ $)$

$8x - 4 =$ _____

$8x -$ _____ $= 6 +$ _____

$2x =$ _____

$x =$ _____ **2 marks**

# ALGEBRA  Equations 2

**1** Solve the equation $2(x - 7) = 20$

_____ **1 mark**

**2** Solve these equations.

**a** $3(x + 8) = 21$

_____ **1 mark**

**b** $3(x - 8) = 21$

_____ **1 mark**

**3** Solve these equations.

**a** $4(x - 1) = 6$

_____ **1 mark**

**b** $4(x + 3) = 12$

_____ **1 mark**

**4** Solve the equation $x - 7 = 2x + 3$

_____ **1 mark**

**5** Solve the equation $5x - 8 = 10 + 2x$

_____ **1 mark**

**6** Solve these equations.

**a** $2x + 5 = x - 1$

_____ **1 mark**

**b** $5x - 2 = 2x - 5$

_____ **1 mark**

**c** $2(x + 1) = 5x - 1$

_____ **1 mark**

**d** $4x + 7 = 6x + 4$

_____ **1 mark**

**7** Solve these equations.

**a** $\dfrac{x+2}{5} = 6 + x$

_____ **1 mark**

**b** $\dfrac{x}{5} + 5 = 3 + x$

_____ **1 mark**

**c** $x + \dfrac{3}{5} = 6 - x$

_____ **1 mark**

**d** $5x - 3 = 6 + x$

_____ **1 mark**

**8** The following diagram shows a rectangle.

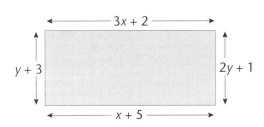

**a** Find the value of $x$.

_____ **1 mark**

**b** Find the value of $y$.

_____ **1 mark**

**9** The diagrams show some bricks. The bricks on the bottom row add up to the value or expression in the top row.

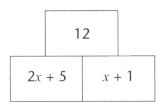

| 12 |
| 2x + 5 | x + 1 |

| 2y − 3 |
| 3y + 1 | y + 6 |

**a** Find the value of $x$.

**b** Find the value of $y$.

_____            _____ **2 marks**

# Trial and improvement

**1** What is the value of $4^3$? _____

**1 mark**

**2** Estimate the value of $3.1^3$. _____

**1 mark**

**3** Estimate the value of $2.7^3 + 3 \times 2.7$. _____

**1 mark**

**4** What is the value of $2^3 + 3 \times 2$? _____

**1 mark**

**5** What is the value of $3.2^3 - 2 \times 3.2$? _____

**1 mark**

**6** A rectangle has sides of $x$ cm and $x + 3$ cm.  It has an area of 40 cm$^2$.

Which of the following must be true?

Tick the correct answer. (There may be more than one.)

**a** ☐ $x(x + 3) = 40$      **b** ☐ The sides are 2 cm and 20 cm

**c** ☐ The sides are 5 cm and 8 cm      **d** ☐ The perimeter is 26 cm

**1 mark**

**7** Complete the table to find a solution to the equation $x^3 = 100$

Give your answer to 1 decimal place.

| $x$ | $x^3$ | Comment |
|---|---|---|
| 4 | 64 | Too low |
| 5 | 125 | Too high |
|  |  |  |
|  |  |  |
|  |  |  |
|  |  |  |
|  |  |  |

$x =$ _____

**3 marks**

**8** Complete the table to find a solution to the equation $x^3 + 3x = 20$

Give your answer to 1 decimal place.

| $x$ | $x^3 + 3x$ | Comment |
|---|---|---|
| 2 | 14 | Too low |
|  |  |  |
|  |  |  |
|  |  |  |
|  |  |  |
|  |  |  |
|  |  |  |

$x =$ _____

**3 marks**

**9** A rectangle has sides of $x$ cm and $x + 2$ cm. It has an area of 16.64 cm$^2$.

  **a**  Explain why $x^2 + 2x = 16.64$

  _____

**1 mark**

  **b**  Complete the table to find the value of $x$.

| $x$ | $x^2 + 2x$ | Comment |
|---|---|---|
| 2 | 8 | Too low |
|  |  |  |
|  |  |  |
|  |  |  |
|  |  |  |
|  |  |  |
|  |  |  |

$x =$ _____

**2 marks**

# SHAPE, SPACE AND MEASURES

## Scales

**1** Read the values from the following scales.

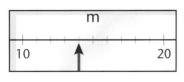

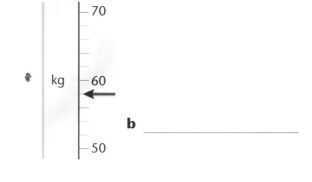

**a** _____

**b** _____

**c** _____

**d** _____

**6 marks**

**e** _____

**f** _____

**2** A melon is weighed.

A melon and a mango are weighed.

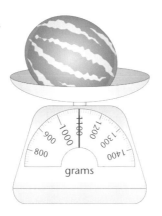

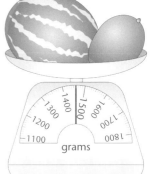

**a** How much does the melon weigh?
Give your answer in kilograms. _____

**1 mark**

**b** How much does the mango weigh?
Give your answer in grams. _____

**1 mark**

**3** How long is there between the time shown on clock A and the time shown on clock B?

Clock A          Clock B

_____

**4** The timetable shows bus times from Barnsley to Millhouse.

| Barnsley | Kingstone | Dodworth | Silkstone | Oxspring | Millhouse |
|----------|-----------|----------|-----------|----------|-----------|
| 10:35    | 10:42     | 11:03    | 11:21     | 11:40    | 12:00     |
| 11:20    | 11:27     | 11:48    | 12:06     | 12:25    | 12:45     |
| 12:42    | 12:49     | 13:10    | 13:28     | 13:47    | 14:07     |

**a** What time does the 10:35 arrive in Oxspring? _____

**b** How long does the 10:35 take to get from Barnsley to Millhouse? _____

**c** Jack arrives at Barnsley bus station at 11 o'clock.

  **i** How long does he have to wait for a bus to Silkstone?

_____

  **ii** How long does the bus take to get to Silkstone?

_____

**5** On a visit to his doctor, Mr Sutcliffe has his height measured.

How tall is Mr Sutcliffe? Give your answer in metres.

_____

1 mark

# SHAPE, SPACE AND MEASURES

# Metric units

1  The table shows how much a carrier charges to deliver parcels.

| Weight up to | Cost |
|---|---|
| 2 kg | £5.00 |
| 5 kg | £8.00 |
| 10 kg | £10.00 |
| 20 kg | £15.00 |

Imogen has three packages to be delivered.
The packages weigh 1.5 kg, 4 kg and 8 kg.

**a**  How much do the three packages weigh altogether?

_____ kg

1 mark

**b**  How much will it cost to deliver all three packages?

£ _____

1 mark

**c**  If Imogen puts all three packages together as a single package, how much cheaper will it be to deliver this single package than three separate packages?

£ _____

1 mark

2  A small cola glass holds 125 ml. How many glasses can be filled from a 75 cl bottle of cola?

_____ glasses

1 mark

3  Complete the following metric relationships.

| Mass | Volume | Length |
|---|---|---|
| $3\frac{1}{4}$ kg = _____ g | 650 cl = _____ litres | 425 mm = _____ cm |

3 marks

4  When Zoe was born she weighed 3 kg 750 grams.
In her first month she put on 450 grams in weight.
How much did she weigh after one month?
Answer in kilograms and grams.

_____ kg _____ g

1 mark

**5** Large jars of pickled fruit weigh 650 grams.
They are sold in trays of 12 jars.
How much does a tray of 12 jars weigh?
Give your answer in kilograms.

_____ kg

**2 marks**

**6** A 1p coin weighs 3.5 grams.
Mohammed has saved a bag of pennies.
The bag weighs 1.4 kilograms.
How much are the pennies in the bag worth?

£ _____

**2 marks**

**7** Mr Wilson weighs 96 kg.
After dieting he loses $3\frac{1}{4}$ kilograms.
How much does he weigh now?

_____ kg

**1 mark**

**8** Two bottles together have a total volume
of $2\frac{1}{2}$ litres.
The larger bottle is four times the volume
of the smaller bottle.
What is the volume of the smaller bottle?
State the units of your answer.

_____

**2 marks**

# SHAPE, SPACE AND MEASURES
## Imperial units

**1** How many inches are there in one foot? _____

**1 mark**

**2** How many pints are there in one gallon? _____

**1 mark**

**3** There are 14 ounces in one pound.
How many ounces are there in 4 pounds? _____

**1 mark**

**4** 1 yard is 3 feet. How many feet are there in 22 yards?

_____

**1 mark**

**5** A crate holds 24 pints of milk.
How many gallons of milk are in the crate? _____

**1 mark**

**6** Approximately how many centimetres are there in one inch?

_____

**1 mark**

**7** Approximately how many litres are there in a gallon?

_____

**1 mark**

**8** Marc buys a 4 kg bag of potatoes for his grandmother and he needs to tell her the approximate weight in pounds.

What is a good approximation for the number of pounds in 4 kg?

_____

1 mark

**9** Abigail travels in her car from York to Middlesbrough which is a distance of 50 miles.

She has to convert this distance into kilometres.

What should her answer be?

_____

1 mark

**10** Put these weights in order, with the smallest first.

10 oz    600 g    1 kg    $\frac{1}{2}$ lb

_____

1 mark

**11** A 1p coin weighs 3.5 grams.

Approximately how many pounds does £10 in pennies weigh?

_____

2 marks

**12** Mr Stone is 6 feet tall.

Approximately how tall is he in metres and centimetres?

_____

1 mark

**13** Two bottles are shown.

Which bottle contains the most?

_____

JUICE
2 litres

3 pints

1 mark

# SHAPE, SPACE AND MEASURES

## Measuring angles and bearings

**1** How many degrees are there in a complete turn?

_____

**2** How many degrees are there in a right angle?

_____

**3** What type of angles are shown below?

**a**

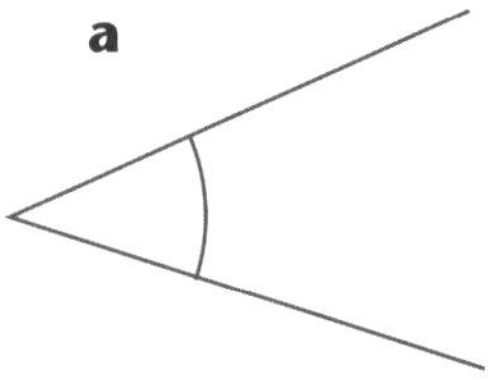

**b**

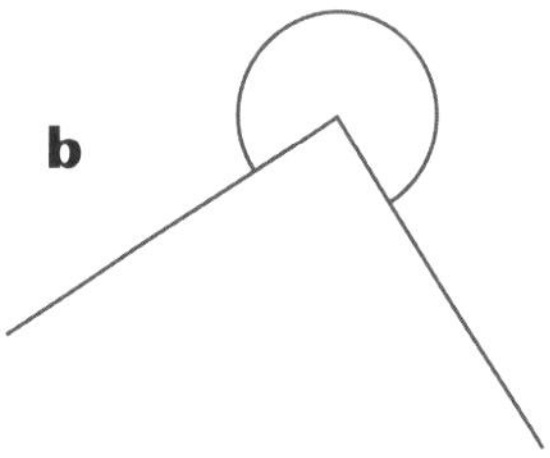

a _____

b _____

**4** Estimate the size of the angles in question 3.

a _____ °

b _____ °

**5** Measure the following angles.

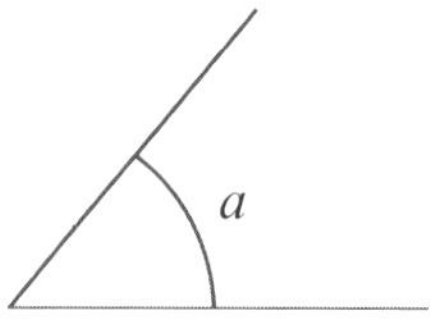

*a*

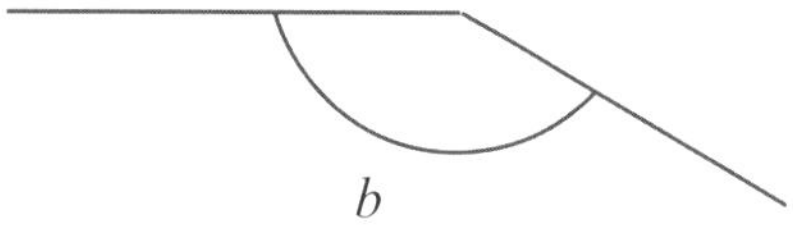

*b*

a _____ °

b _____ °

**6** Draw angles of **a** 75° **b** 160°

**a**

**b**

2 marks

**7** Measure **a** the actual distance **b** the bearing of *A, B* and *C* from *O* in the diagram below.

C.

N

Scale 1 cm: 2 km

• *A*

*O*

*B* •

6 marks

**8** From the point *O* draw the following points.

   **a**   *A* which is 5 cm on a bearing of 065° from *O*

   **b**   *B* which is 4 cm on a bearing of 155° from *O*

   **c**   *C* which is 6 cm on a bearing of 265° from *O*

N

*O*

6 marks

# SHAPE, SPACE AND MEASURES

## Angle facts

**1** What is the size of angle *a* in the diagram?

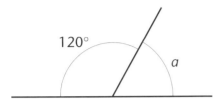

_____ °

1 mark

**2** What is the size of angle *b* in the diagram?

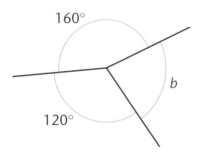

_____ °

1 mark

**3** What is the size of angle *c* in the diagram?

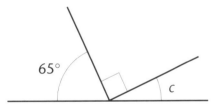

_____ °

1 mark

**4** What is the size of angle *d* in the diagram?

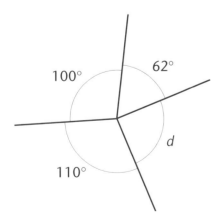

_____ °

1 mark

**5** Calculate the size of angle *e* in the triangle below.

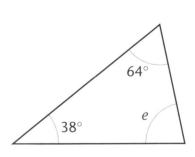

_____ °

1 mark

58

**6** *ABC* is a right-angled triangle. Calculate the value of angle *f*.

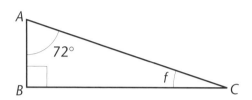

_____ °

**1 mark**

**7** *PQR* is an isosceles triangle. Calculate the value of angle *g*.

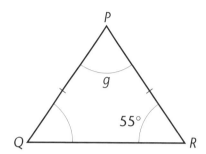

_____ °

**1 mark**

**8** Calculate the size of angle *x*.

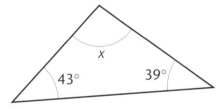

_____ °

**1 mark**

**9** Calculate the size of angle *y*.

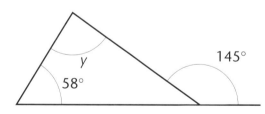

_____ °

**1 mark**

**10** Calculate the size of angle *z*.

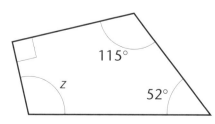

_____ °

**1 mark**

# SHAPE, SPACE AND MEASURES

# Angles in parallel lines and polygons

**1** Write down the values of angles *a*, *b* and *c*.

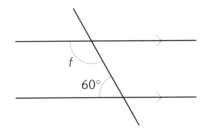

$a =$ _____ $b =$ _____ $c =$ _____

**3 marks**

**2** Write down the value of angle *d*. Give a reason for your answer.

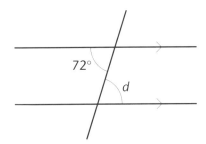

$d =$ _____ because _____

**2 marks**

**3** Write down the value of angle *e*. Give a reason for your answer.

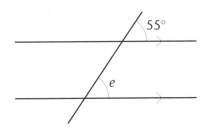

$e =$ _____ because _____

**2 marks**

**4** Write down the value of angle *f*. Give a reason for your answer.

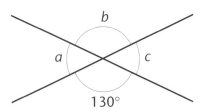

$f =$ _____ because _____

**2 marks**

**5** Write down the value of angles *g* and *h*. Give reasons for your answers.

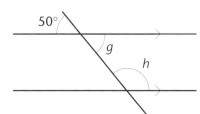

50°

*g*

*h*

*g* = _____ because _____

*h* = _____ because _____

**2 marks**

**6** What is the sum of the interior angles of a pentagon? _____ °

**1 mark**

**7** Which of the following statements is true for a regular hexagon?
Tick the correct answer. (There may be more than one.)

☐ Each interior angle is 60°   ☐ Each interior angle is 120˚

☐ Each exterior angle is 60˚   ☐ Each exterior angle is 120˚

**1 mark**

**8** *ABCDE* is a regular pentagon.
Work out the value of angles *x*, *y* and *z*.

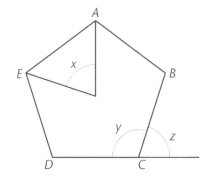

*x* = _____ *y* = _____

*z* = _____

**3 marks**

**9** The diagram shows four regular octagons, A, B, C and D.
Explain why shape S is a square.

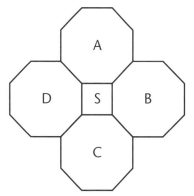

_____

_____

_____

**2 marks**

# SHAPE, SPACE AND MEASURES

## Symmetry

**1** How many lines of symmetry does a rectangle have? _____

1 mark

**2** What is the order of rotational symmetry for a square? _____

1 mark

**3** How many lines of symmetry does an isosceles triangle have?

_____

1 mark

**4** What is the order of rotational symmetry for a kite? _____

1 mark

**5** Which of the following statements is true for a parallelogram?
Tick the correct statement. (There may be more than one.)

☐ It has no lines of symmetry.

☐ It has rotational symmetry of order 1.

☐ It has 1 line of symmetry.

☐ It has rotational symmetry of order 2.

1 mark

**6** **a** On the star below, draw on all the lines of symmetry.

1 mark

    **b** What is the order of rotational symmetry of the star?
Mark the centre of rotation on the diagram.

1 mark

**7** For each of these capital letters, write down **i** the number of lines of symmetry and
**ii** the order of rotational symmetry.

   **a** **H** **i** lines _____ **ii** order _____

   **b** **N** **i** lines _____ **ii** order _____

   **c** **S** **i** lines _____ **ii** order _____

   **d** **Y** **i** lines _____ **ii** order _____

**4 marks**

**8** Shade one more square on the diagram
so that it has two lines of symmetry and
rotational symmetry of order 2.

**1 mark**

**9** Look at this series of stars. For each one, write down
   **i** the number of lines of symmetry
   **ii** the order of rotational symmetry

**a**   **b**   **c**   **d** 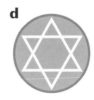  **e**

   **i** _____   _____   _____   _____   _____

**5 marks**

   **ii** _____   _____   _____   _____   _____

**5 marks**

**10** Shade five more squares so that the grid
has rotational symmetry of order 4.

**1 mark**

# SHAPE, SPACE AND MEASURES

## Reflections and rotations

levels **4-6**

**1** Reflect the triangle in the mirror line.

**1 mark**

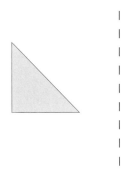

**2** Reflect the trapezium in the mirror line.

**1 mark**

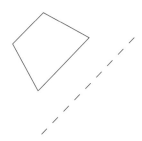

**3** Arrow X is rotated clockwise onto arrow Y about the point *O*.

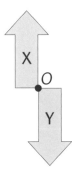

What is the angle of rotation?

____________________

**1 mark**

**4** The rectangle R is rotated anticlockwise onto rectangle S about the point *O*.

What is the angle of rotation?

____________________

**1 mark**

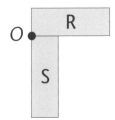

**5** Shape A is rotated onto each of the shapes B, C and D.
In each case give **i** the angle of rotation
**ii** the direction of rotation   **iii** the centre of rotation.

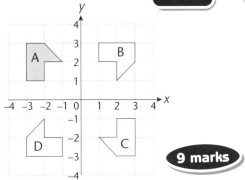

**B i** _____ **ii** _____ **iii** _____

**C i** _____ **ii** _____ **iii** _____

**D i** _____ **ii** _____ **iii** _____

**9 marks**

**6** Shape A is reflected one onto each of the shapes B, C and D.
In each case give the equation of the mirror line.

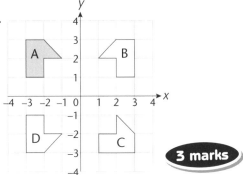

**B** _____

**C** _____

**D** _____

**3 marks**

**7** Triangle $ABC$ is reflected in the line $y = x$
onto triangle $A'B'C'$.
   **a** Write down the coordinates of

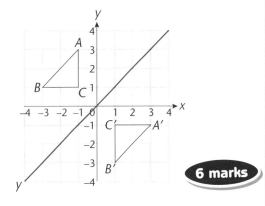

$A$ ( _____ , _____ )     $A'$ ( _____ , _____ )

$B$ ( _____ , _____ )     $B'$ ( _____ , _____ )

$C$ ( _____ , _____ )     $C'$ ( _____ , _____ )

**6 marks**

   **b** What do you notice about each pair of coordinates
   (e.g. $A$ and $A'$)?

   _____

**1 mark**

**8** Triangles B, C, D and E are all rotations of triangle A.
Match the triangle with the description below.

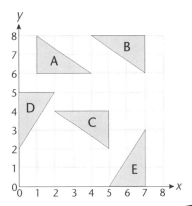

   **i**   Half turn about (3, 5) is triangle _____

   **ii**  Quarter turn anticlockwise about (7, 6) is triangle

   _____

   **iii** Quarter turn clockwise about (0, 6) is triangle

   _____

   **iv**  Half turn about (4, 7) is triangle _____

**4 marks**

# SHAPE, SPACE AND MEASURES

## Enlargements

level
6

**1** Shapes A and B are enlargements of the shaded shape.

What is the scale factor of each enlargement?

A _____

B _____

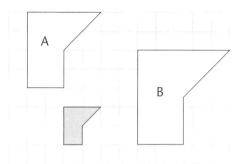

**2 marks**

**2** The white shape is an enlargement of the shaded shape with scale factor 2. One 'ray' joining similar points is shown.

Draw the other rays to find the centre of enlargement.

**1 mark**

**3** On the grid, draw an enlargement of the triangle with a scale factor of 2.

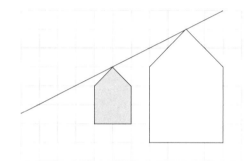

**1 mark**

**4** On the grid, draw an enlargement of the shape with a scale factor of 3.

**1 mark**

**5** The triangle *ABC* is enlarged to a triangle *A'B'C'* by a scale factor of 2 about the origin.

Write down the coordinates of the points *A'*, *B'* and *C'*.

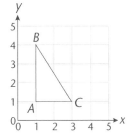

*A'* ( _____ , _____ )

*B'* ( _____ , _____ )

*C'* ( _____ , _____ )

**3 marks**

**6** The triangle *A'B'C'* has been enlarged from a triangle *ABC* by a scale factor of 3 about the origin.

Write down the coordinates of the points *A*, *B* and *C*.

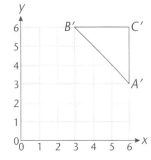

*A* ( _____ , _____ )

*B* ( _____ , _____ )

*C* ( _____ , _____ )

**3 marks**

**7** The shaded triangle has been transformed to triangles A, B and C.

Match the triangle to the transformation described below.

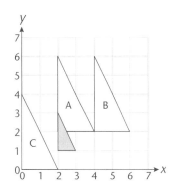

**a** Enlargement scale factor 2 about (0, 0) is

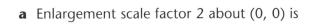

**b** Enlargement scale factor 2 about (2, 0) is

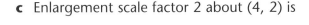

**c** Enlargement scale factor 2 about (4, 2) is

**3 marks**

67

# SHAPE, SPACE AND MEASURES

## 3-D shapes

**1** Write down the names of these solids.

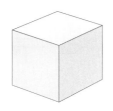  

 **3 marks**

_____    _____    _____

**2** How many **a** edges, **b** faces and **c** vertices does a cuboid have?

**a** _____

**b** _____

**c** _____    **3 marks**

**3** How many **a** edges, **b** faces and **c** vertices does a square-based pyramid have?

**a** _____

**b** _____

**c** _____    **3 marks**

**4** Look at the net.
What is the name of the shape that will be formed by this net?

_____    **1 mark**

**5** Which of the following are nets for a cube?

**a**     **b**     **c** 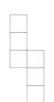    **d**     _____

**1 mark**

**6** This is the plan and elevation for a solid.
What is the name of this solid?

_____    **1 mark**

PLAN          ELEVATION

**7** For this solid, draw
   **a** the plan
   **b** the elevation from X
   **c** the elevation from Y

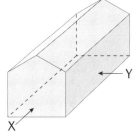

**3 marks**

**8** How many planes of symmetry do the following shapes have?

**a**

**b**

**c**

**3 marks**

_____   _____   _____

**9** The shape shown is made from six centimetre cubes.
   Draw   **a** the plan
         **b** the elevation from A

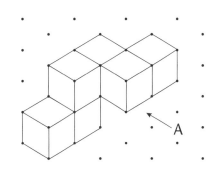

**2 marks**

**10** A shape is made from four centimetre cubes.
   The plan and two side elevations are shown below.

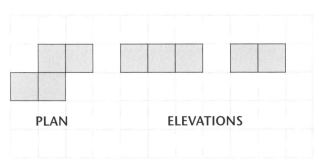

PLAN          ELEVATIONS

Draw an isometric view of the shape.

**2 marks**

# SHAPE, SPACE AND MEASURES

## Perimeter and area

**1** What is the perimeter of this shape?

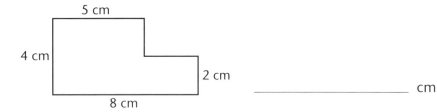

_____ cm

**2** What is the perimeter of this shape?
Remember to include the units in
your answer.

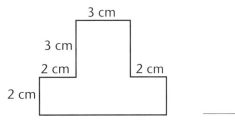

_____

**3** What is the area of this rectangle?

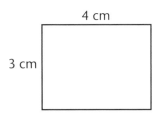

_____

**4** What is **a** the perimeter and **b** the area of this right-angled triangle?

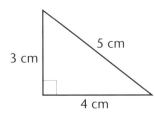

**a** perimeter _____

**b** area _____

**5** Work out **a** the perimeter and **b** the area of this isosceles triangle.
Remember to include the units in your answer.

    **a** perimeter_____

    **b** area_____

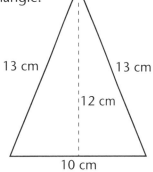

13 cm       13 cm

12 cm

10 cm

**3 marks**

**6** A, B, C and D are triangles drawn on a centimetre grid.
What are the areas of triangles A, B, C and D?

A _____ cm²

B _____ cm²

C _____ cm²

D _____ cm²

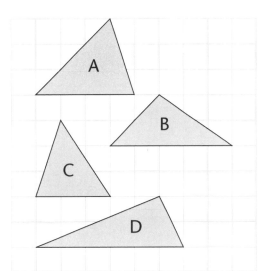

**4 marks**

**7** What is the area of this parallelogram?

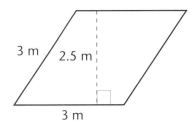

3 m   2.5 m

3 m

_____

**2 marks**

**8** What is the area of this trapezium?

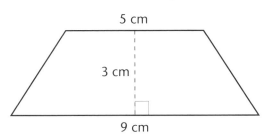

5 cm

3 cm

9 cm

_____

**2 marks**

# Circumference and area of a circle

level
6

**1** The diameter of a circle is 5 cm.
What is its circumference? Give your answer to 1 decimal place.

_____ cm

1 mark

**2** The radius of a circle is 4 m.
What is its circumference? Give your answer to 1 decimal place.

_____ m

1 mark

**3** The circumference of a circle is 25 cm.
What is its diameter? Give your answer to the nearest centimetre.

_____ cm

1 mark

**4** A tin of beans has a diameter of 7.5 cm.
The label around the tin has an overlap of 1 cm.
What is the length of the label?
Give your answer to 1 decimal place.
Remember to include the units in your answer.

_____

2 marks

**5** What is the perimeter of this semicircle?
Give your answer to 1 decimal place.

_____ cm

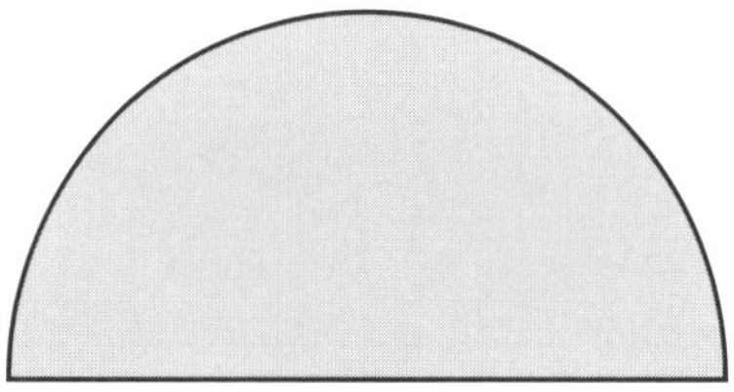

10 cm

1 mark

**6** The radius of a circle is 3 cm.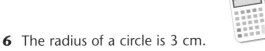
What is its area? Give your answer to 1 decimal place.

_____ cm²

**1 mark**

**7** The diameter of a circle is 5 cm.
What is its area?
Remember to include the units in your answer.

_____

**2 marks**

**8** A circle has a diameter of 18 cm.
What is its area?
Give your answer as a multiple of π.

_____ cm²

**1 mark**

**9** What is the area of this quadrant?
Give your answer to 1 decimal place.

8 cm

8 cm

_____ cm²

**1 mark**

**10** What is the area of the shaded part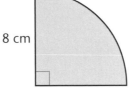
of the diagram?
Give your answer to 1 decimal place.

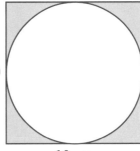

10 cm

10 cm

_____ cm²

**1 mark**

# SHAPE, SPACE AND MEASURES

## Volume

**1**  What is the volume of this cuboid?

_____ cm³

2 cm

3 cm

8 cm

**1 mark**

**2**  **a**  What is the volume of this cuboid?

_____ cm³

**b**  What is the surface area?

_____ cm²

5 cm

3 cm

1 cm

**1 mark**

**1 mark**

**3**  A cuboid has a volume of 36 cm³.
Its length is 6 cm and its width is 3 cm.
What is the height of the cuboid?

_____ cm

**1 mark**

**4**  A cuboid has a volume of 200 cm³.
Its length and width are 5 cm.
What is the surface area?
Remember to include the units in your answer.

_____

**2 marks**

**5**  The volume of a cube is 64 cm³.
What is the length of each edge of the cube?

_____ cm

**1 mark**

**6** The surface area of this cuboid is 184 cm². Work out the length of the cuboid.

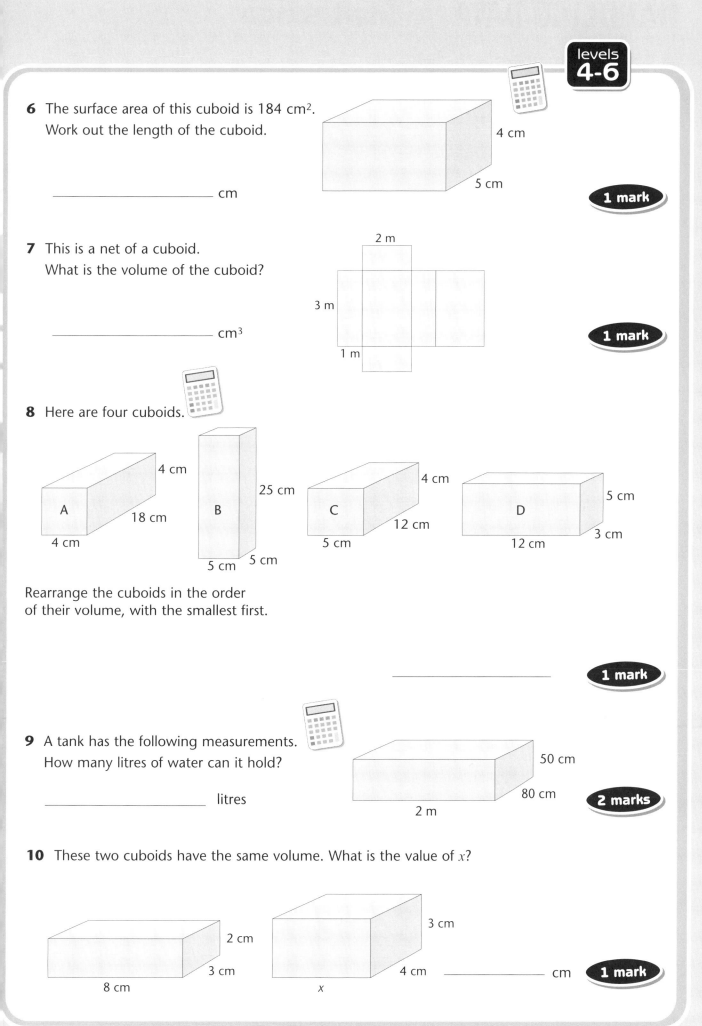

4 cm

5 cm

_____ cm

**1 mark**

**7** This is a net of a cuboid.
What is the volume of the cuboid?

2 m

3 m

1 m

_____ cm³

**1 mark**

**8** Here are four cuboids.

4 cm

A

18 cm

4 cm

25 cm

B

5 cm 5 cm

4 cm

C

5 cm

12 cm

5 cm

D

12 cm

3 cm

Rearrange the cuboids in the order
of their volume, with the smallest first.

_____

**1 mark**

**9** A tank has the following measurements.
How many litres of water can it hold?

50 cm

80 cm

2 m

_____ litres

**2 marks**

**10** These two cuboids have the same volume. What is the value of *x*?

2 cm

3 cm

8 cm

3 cm

4 cm

*x*

_____ cm **1 mark**

# HANDLING DATA  Statistics

**1** The table shows the number of passengers queuing for the local bus each morning for a month.

| Passengers | Tally | Frequency |
|---|---|---|
| 12 | \|\|\|\| | 4 |
| 13 | ┼┼┼┼ \|\| | 7 |
| 14 | | 8 |
| 15 | | 6 |
| 16 | \|\| | |
| 17 | \| | |

**a** Complete the Tally column.

**b** Complete the Frequency column.

**c** Explain why you know the month chosen was February.

_____

_____

**2** The number of marks scored on a tables test by 30 members of form 9H are:

7  6    5  7    3  5    7  8    9  4    4  10    9    7    5
5    6    10    9    8    7    5    4    7    6    4    8    3    6    7

**a** Complete the frequency table below.

| Score | Tally | Frequency |
|---|---|---|
| 3 | | |
| 4 | | |
| 5 | | |
| 6 | | |
| 7 | | |
| 8 | | |
| 9 | | |
| 10 | | |

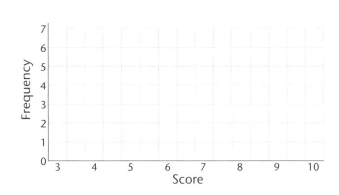

**b** What was the modal score? _____

**c** Draw a bar chart to show the data.

**3** What is the mode from this list of numbers?

2    3    4    3    4    2    5    3    2    4    3    4    5    3

_____

**4** The number of marbles in 10 packets is as follows:

11    12    13    11    12    14    17    15    14    12

**a** What is the range? _____

**b** What is the mode? _____

**5** The ages of a junior hockey team are as follows:

13   14   12   14   12   14   9   13   12   10   12

   **a** What is the modal age? _____

1 mark

   **b** What is the range of the ages? _____

1 mark

**6** This frequency table shows the number of visits to the cinema by 30 students over a one-month period.

| No. of visits | Frequency |
|:---:|:---:|
| 0 | 8 |
| 1 | 10 |
| 2 | 6 |
| 3 | 4 |
| 4 | 2 |
| Total | 30 |

   **a** Write down the modal number of visits.

   _____

1 mark

   **b** Write down the range of the number of visits.

   _____

1 mark

**7** This bar chart shows the midday temperature in London during one month.

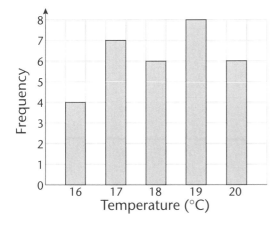

   **a** For how many days was the temperature recorded? _____

1 mark

   **b** What is the modal temperature? _____

1 mark

   **c** What is the range of the temperature?_____

1 mark

   **d** The month recorded was either July or January.
     Which was it?

   _____

1 mark

# HANDLING DATA

## Mode, median and mean

**1** What is the median for this list of numbers?

5  10  8  8  5  4  8  6  7

_____

1 mark

**2** What is the mean for this set of numbers?

23  32  42  38  21  26  30  28  _____

1 mark

**3** The number of sweets in 10 packets are as follows:

34  35  36  37  38  38  38  39  39  40

Work out **a** the mode, **b** the median and **c** the mean.

**a** _____

1 mark

**b** _____

1 mark

**c** _____

1 mark

**4** The ages of a football team are as follows:

23  24  22  24  18  24  19  23  26  20  19

Work out **a** the mode, **b** the median and **c** the mean.

**a** _____

1 mark

**b** _____

1 mark

**c** _____

1 mark

**5** This frequency table shows the number of letters in 40 words taken from a passage in a magazine. Work out **a** the mode, **b** the median and **c** the mean.

| No. of letters | Frequency |
|:---:|:---:|
| 1 | 4 |
| 2 | 5 |
| 3 | 9 |
| 4 | 7 |
| 5 | 6 |
| 6 | 6 |
| 7 | 3 |
| **Total** | 40 |

**a** _____

1 mark

**b** _____

1 mark

**c** _____

1 mark

78

**6** This bar chart shows the number of merits in a week for a class of Year 9 students.

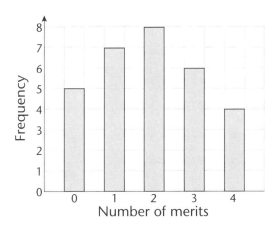

Number of merits

**a** How many students are in the class?

_____

**1 mark**

**b** What is the modal number of merits?

_____

**1 mark**

**c** What is the total number of merits?

_____

**1 mark**

**d** What is the mean number of merits?

_____

**1 mark**

**7** This grouped frequency table shows the ages of 50 members of a tennis club.

Which of the following statements could be true and which must be false?

| Age | Frequency |
|---|---|
| 21 – 30 | 15 |
| 31 – 40 | 18 |
| 41 – 50 | 12 |
| 51 – 60 | 4 |
| 61 – 70 | 1 |
| **Total** | 50 |

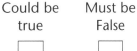

Could be true    Must be False

**a** The median age is 45. ☐ ☐

**b** The modal age is 65. ☐ ☐

**c** The modal age is 49. ☐ ☐

**3 marks**

**8** The bar charts show the number of days absent in a week for students in two different classes in Year 10.

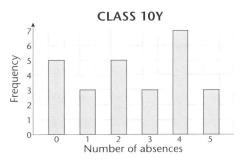

CLASS 10X                CLASS 10Y

Number of absences         Number of absences

**a** State the modal number of absences for each class. 10X _____ 10Y _____

**2 marks**

**b** Work out the median number of absences for each class. 10X _____ 10Y _____

**2 marks**

**c** Work out the mean number of absences for each class. 10X _____ 10Y _____

**2 marks**

**d** Which class was worse for absentees? Give a reason for your answer.

_____

**1 mark**

# HANDLING DATA

## Comparing distributions

**1** The table shows information about two sets of data.

|        | Mean | Range |
|--------|------|-------|
| Set A  | 12   | 8     |
| Set B  | 12   | 3     |

Which set is the more consistent?

_____

**2** Find three numbers with a mode of 6 and a mean of 7. _____

**3** Find three numbers with a median of 5, a mean of 6 and a range of 5.

_____

**4** Three numbers have a mode of 8 and a range of 6.
Write down two possible sets of data for which this is possible.

_____ and _____

**5** The table shows information about how late two buses are over a 20-day period.
The data is in minutes.

|        | Mean | Median | Mode | Range |
|--------|------|--------|------|-------|
| Bus A  | 8    | 9      | 3    | 15    |
| Bus B  | 8    | 4      | 0    | 10    |

Which bus is the most reliable?
Give a reason for your answer.

_____

_____

**2 marks**

**6** The following data shows the weekly wages in a small factory with 8 workers.
£95   £220   £220   £220   £220   £220   £320   £700
Which of the following is true for the data?
Tick the correct answer. (There may be more than one.)

**a** ☐ The mean is not a good average to use as it is affected by the large value.

**b** ☐ The mode is a representative average.

**c** ☐ The range of £605 shows that there are a wide variety of different wages in the factory.

**d** ☐ The range of £605 shows that the data is inconsistent.

**1 mark**

**7** The following data shows the weekly wages in a small factory with 8 workers.

£95   £220   £220   £220   £220   £220   £320   £700

Everyone gets a £20 a week pay rise.

Which of the following is true for the new wages?

Tick the correct answer. (There may be on more than one.)

**a** ☐ The mean will increase by £20.

**b** ☐ The mode will increase by £20.

**c** ☐ The median will increase by £20.

**d** ☐ The range will increase by £20.

1 mark

**8** Two girls want to be in the school senior netball team.

The number of goals they scored in their last 10 junior matches was:

Aisha   3   7   2   4   4   1   1   0   2   1

Sarah   3   4   2   3   3   1   2   2   3   2

**a** Work out the mean number of goals for each girl. _____

2 marks

**b** Work out the range for each girl. _____

2 marks

**c** Which girl should be chosen for the senior team and why?

_____

1 mark

**9** The data shows the number of tomatoes from 10 plants grown in a greenhouse and 10 plants grown outside.

Greenhouse   5   8   7   12   4   6   9   10   8   4

Outside        5   5   8   9   8   6   6   9   8   6

**a** Work out the mean number of tomatoes per plant for

**i** the greenhouse _____

**ii** outside _____

2 marks

**b** Work out the range for the number of tomatoes per plant for

**i** the greenhouse _____

**ii** outside _____

2 marks

**c** Which is the better place to grow tomatoes and why?

_____

1 mark

**1** The graph shows the trend in the temperature in a garden over a week in May. The readings were taken at midday each day.

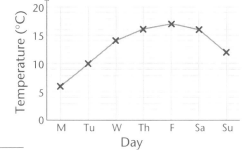

**a** What was the temperature on Wednesday?

_____

1 mark

**b** The temperature was 16 °C on 2 days.

Which days? _____ and _____

1 mark

**c** On what day was the temperature highest? _____

1 mark

**d** Explain why you cannot tell what the temperature was at midnight on Wednesday. _____

1 mark

**2** The graph shows the trend in the temperature in a garden over a week. The temperatures were recorded at 12 midday and 12 midnight.

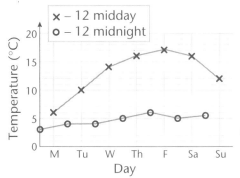

**a** What was the temperature at midnight and midday on Monday?

midnight _____ midday _____

1 mark

**b** What was the difference in temperatures between midday and midnight on Tuesday? _____

1 mark

**c** Which day had the greatest difference between the temperatures at midday and midnight? _____

1 mark

**3** The graph shows the miles travelled each month by a lorry driver.

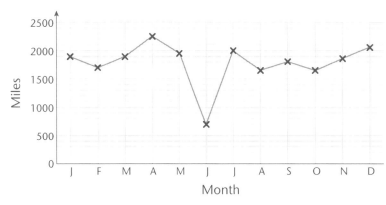

**a** What was the distance he travelled in January? _____

1 mark

**b** What was the total distance travelled in the first three months of the year?

_____

1 mark

**c** Which month was he most likely to be on holiday? _____

1 mark

levels 5-6

**4** The graph shows the results of an experiment to see if a detergent has any effect on bacteria. Results were recorded every hour from 10 am to 4 pm.

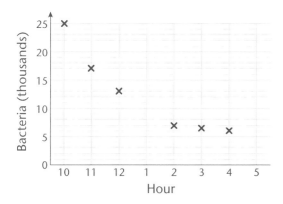

**a** The scientist was at lunch at 1 pm.
Estimate the number of bacteria at 1 pm.
Give your answer to the nearest 100. ______________________

**1 mark**

**b** When the number of bacteria drop below 5000 the detergent is said to be effective.
The scientist claimed that this graph shows that this detergent is effective.
Is this claim true or false? Give a reason for your answer.

______________________________________________

______________________________________________

**1 mark**

**c** Is it possible to estimate the number of bacteria at 11.30 am?
Give a reason for your answer.

______________________________________________

______________________________________________

**1 mark**

**5** The graph shows the depth of water in a drain during a heavy rainstorm.
When the depth gets to 30 cm the area will flood.
John predicts that the area will flood by 2 pm.
Is this claim justified? Explain your answer.

______________________________________________

______________________________________________

______________________________________________

**1 mark**

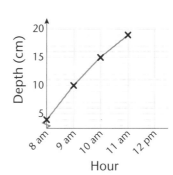

**1** This pie chart shows the proportion of boys and girls in a youth club.

What is the ratio of boys to girls?

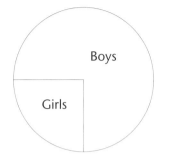

Boys

Girls

1 mark

_____

**2** The table shows information on the makes of 36 cars in a car park.

Complete the column for the angle that each make would have on a pie chart.

| Make | Frequency | Angle |
|------|-----------|-------|
| Ford | 8 | |
| Vauxhall | 3 | |
| Toyota | 7 | |
| **Total** | **18** | |

2 marks

**3** The table shows information on colours of cars in a car park.

| Colour | Frequency | Angle |
|--------|-----------|-------|
| Blue | 9 | |
| White | 4 | |
| Silver | 7 | |
| **Total** | **20** | |

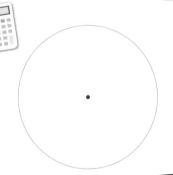

**a** Complete the column for the angle that each colour would have on a pie chart.

2 marks

**b** Draw a pie chart to show the information.

2 marks

**4** Look at the pie chart which shows the favourite pets of some students.

Fifty students were surveyed altogether.

How many students preferred rabbits?

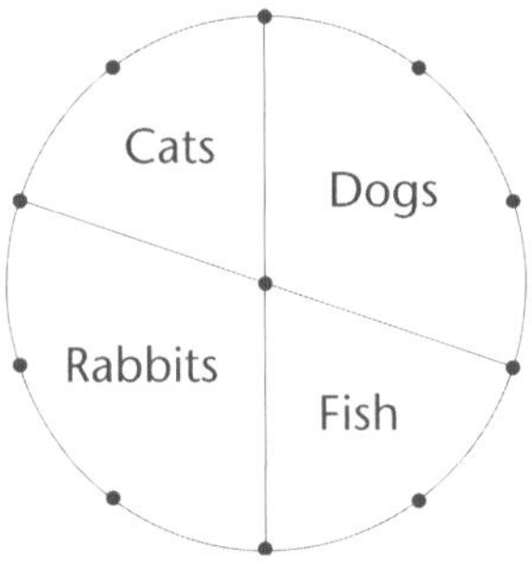

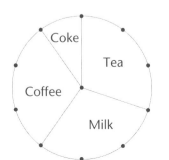

Cats

Dogs

Rabbits

Fish

1 mark

_____

**5** Look at the pie chart which shows the favourite drinks of some people.

48 students chose coffee.

How many students altogether were in the survey?

Coke

Tea

Coffee

Milk

1 mark

_____

**6** The pie chart shows the results of an election survey.
It is not drawn accurately.
120 people said they would vote Labour.
How many people said they would vote Green?

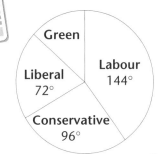

_____

**1 mark**

**7** Which of the following could not be the angles of the sectors in a pie chart?

Tick the correct answer.

**a** ☐ 90°, 60°, 130°, 80°    **b** ☐ 75°, 25°, 200°, 60°

**c** ☐ 62°, 144°, 96°, 48°    **d** ☐ 90°, 90°, 90°, 90°

**1 mark**

**8** Emma did a survey about the month people were born in.
She surveyed 240 people.
Which of the following would be a valid reason why a pie chart is not a good method of representing the data?
Tick the correct answer.

**a** ☐ There are too many sectors to show a valid comparison.

**b** ☐ 240 doesn't divide into 360 exactly.

**c** ☐ People might lie about their birthday.

**d** ☐ You couldn't fit the labels on the pie chart.

**1 mark**

**9** The table shows information about the nationality of people on a plane.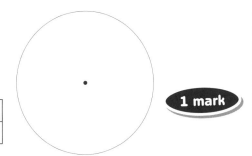
Draw a pie chart to represent the data.

**1 mark**

|  | British | American | French | German |
|---|---|---|---|---|
| **Percentage** | 45% | 25% | 20% | 10% |

**10** Draw a pie chart to represent this data.

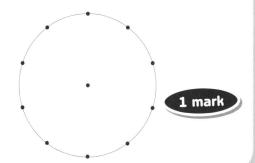

| Blue | Silver | Black |
|---|---|---|
| 12 | 6 | 2 |

**1 mark**

**1** The table shows the heights of some plants in a greenhouse.

| Height, $h$ (cm) | Tally | Frequency |
|---|---|---|
| $0 < h \leq 10$ | ⵌ ⵌ I | |
| $10 < h \leq 20$ | ⵌ IIII | |
| $20 < h \leq 30$ | ⵌ I | |
| $30 < h \leq 40$ | IIII | |

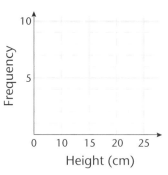

    **a**   Complete the Frequency column.

    **b**   Draw a frequency diagram for the data.

**1 mark**

**1 mark**

**2** The frequency diagram shows the marks
obtained by a class in a test.

    **a**   How many students are in the class?

    _____

    **b**   How many students got a mark over 50?

    _____

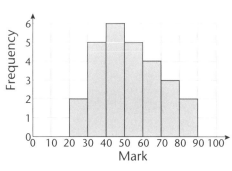

    **c**   If the teacher gave a merit for all students who scored
over 85, how many students would get a merit? _____

**1 mark**

**1 mark**

**1 mark**

**3** This frequency diagram shows the speeds of 100 cars on a motorway.
Which of the following statements is true for the data?
Tick the correct answer. (There may be more than one.)

    **a**   ☐   The average speed is between 50 and 90 mph.

    **b**   ☐   The median speed is between 60 and 70 mph.

    **c**   ☐   The modal speed is between 60 and 70 mph.

    **d**   ☐   The range of the speeds is between 20 and 40 mph.

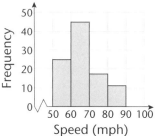

**1 mark**

**4** The data shows the number of e-mails received over 15 days.

7, 12, 22, 17, 11, 9, 8, 13, 15, 21, 19, 18, 8, 8, 13

Show the data in a stem-and-leaf diagram using the key 1 | 2 represents 12.

**1 mark**

**5** The dual bar chart shows the number of days absences for boys and girls in Years 7 to 11 for one week.

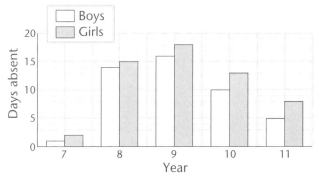

**a** How many boys in Year 9 were absent? _____

**b** Which year has the least absence? _____

**c** How many girls were absent altogether? _____

**d** How many students were absent altogether? _____

1 mark

**6** The table shows information about lengths of the leaves on a plant.

| Length, $x$ (cm) | Frequency |
|---|---|
| $0 < x \leq 5$ | 10 |
| $5 < x \leq 10$ | 17 |
| $10 < x \leq 15$ | 14 |
| $15 < x \leq 20$ | 9 |

Draw a frequency diagram to show this data.

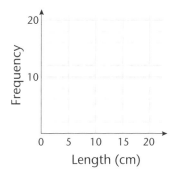

1 mark

**7** The stem-and-leaf diagram shows the ages of 12 members of a chess club.

Key:  1 | 3 represents 13 years.

```
1 | 3   8   9
2 | 0   2   2   2   3   5   8
3 | 1   4
```

**a** How old is the oldest member? _____

**b** What is the modal age of the members? _____

**c** What is the range of the ages of the members? _____

1 mark

**1** Correlation can be described using the following terms:

**S**   Strong positive correlation      **W**   Weak positive correlation

**N**   No correlation

**G**   Strong negative correlation      **K**   Weak negative correlation

**a**   Match each diagram with one of the descriptions above.

*4 marks*

i    ii    iii    iv

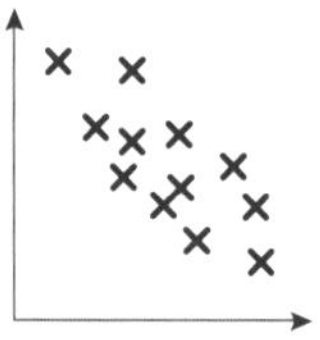

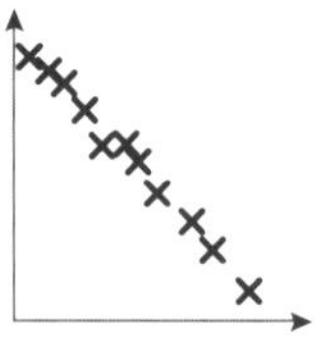

**b**   Match the types of correlation to these comparisons.

**i**   The age of a car and its top speed. _____

**ii**   The number of men building a wall and the time taken to build it. _____

**iii**   The number of ice creams sold and the temperature. _____

**iv**   The value of cars and their age. _____

*4 marks*

**2** The scatter graph shows the heights and weights of a breed of horses.

**a**   Draw a line of best fit on the data.

*1 mark*

**b**   A horse of the same breed has a weight of 232 kg. Estimate its height.

_____

*1 mark*

**c**   Another horse has a weight of 200 kg and is 200 cm tall.

Could this horse be of the same breed?

Give a reason for your answer.

_____

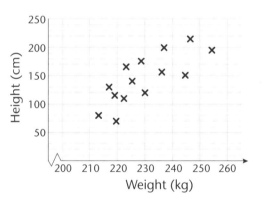

*1 mark*

**3** The graph shows the finishing times of runners in a marathon and the number of miles run per week in training. A line of best fit has been drawn.

Neil runs 120 miles a week in training.

What is his likely finishing time?

_____

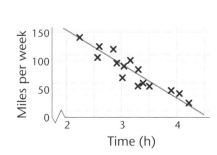

*1 mark*

**4** The scatter graph shows the ages and number of years in the job for the men and women employed in a do-it-yourself store.

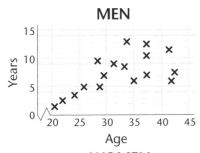

MEN

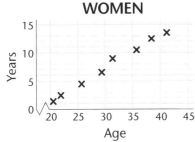

WOMEN

Which of the following statements is true for the data?
Tick the correct answer. (There may be more than one.)

**a** ☐ The women's scatter graph shows strong positive correlation.

**b** ☐ The men's scatter graph shows strong positive correlation.

**c** ☐ There are more men employed than women.

**d** ☐ For men over 30 there is no correlation between their age and the number of years employed.

 1 mark

**5** Three different variables are:

**A** the time it takes to plaster a wall

**B** the number of men working on a job

**C** the weekly wage bill

Which of the following will be true?
Tick the correct answer. (There may be more than one.)

**a** ☐ A and B will show negative correlation.

**b** ☐ A and C will show no correlation.

**c** ☐ B and C will show negative correlation.

**d** ☐ B and C will show positive correlation.

1 mark

**6** The scatter graph shows the ages and finishing times in a marathon for 10 members of a running club.

**a** Describe the correlation.

_____

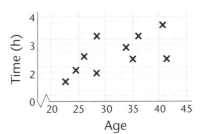

1 mark

**b** Draw a line of best fit on the data.

1 mark

**c** Another member of the club is 45 years old.
What is his likely finishing time?

_____

 1 mark

# HANDLING DATA   Surveys

**1** When carrying out a survey, which of the following should you do?
Tick the correct answer. (There may be more than one.)

**a** ☐ Ask friends, relatives or neighbours.

**b** ☐ Ask a variety of people.

**c** ☐ Ask questions that are unbiased.

**d** ☐ Make sure there is an equal number of boys and girls.

*1 mark*

**2** Jodie does a survey to find out people's views on the following question.
**'Should school uniform be worn by all students?'**

**a** Say why each of the following would not be good responses to this question.

**i**

| Yes ☐ | No ☐ |

Criticism _____
_____

*1 mark*

**ii**

| Agree ☐ | Don't know ☐ | Disagree ☐ |

Criticism _____

*1 mark*

**iii**

| Ties ☐ | Blazers ☐ | Shoes ☐ | Caps ☐ |

Criticism _____

*1 mark*

**b** Say why this is a good response to the same question.

| Strongly agree ☐ | Agree somewhat ☐ | Neither agree nor disagree ☐ | Disagree somewhat ☐ | Strongly Disagree ☐ |

Reason _____

*1 mark*

**3** Give two reasons why this is not a good survey question.
**'People who smoke are not very intelligent. Don't you agree?'**

Reason 1 _____

*1 mark*

Reason 2 _____

*1 mark*

**4** Four students are doing a survey on sport.
Asif decides to ask 30 students in the Badminton club.
Benny decides to ask his Year 9 tutor group.
Colin decides to ask 30 students on the school field at lunchtime.
Derek gets a list of all the students in school and randomly selects 30 names to ask.
Who will get the most reliable results? Give a reason for your answer.

Reason _____

*1 mark*

**5** What is wrong with this question on eye colour?

| What is your eye colour? | **Brown** Yes/No | **Blue** Yes/No |

Reason _____

**6** The headmaster gets an alphabetical list of all the students in the school and sends a questionnaire to every tenth name on the list.
Explain why this will give a good sample of the students.

Reason _____

**7** In a clothing factory there are 100 women employees and 15 men employees.
The managing director sends a questionnaire to the men and 15 of the women.
Explain why this will not give a representative sample.

Reason _____

**8** Jade does a survey to find out people's views on the following question.
**'Did you learn anything from the lesson?'**

   **a** Say why each of the following would not be good responses to this question.

    **i**

| Yes ☐ | No ☐ |

     Criticism _____

     _____

    **ii**

| A bit ☐ | Don't know ☐ | A lot ☐ |

     Criticism _____

     _____

    **iii**

| Pythagoras ☐ | Trigonometry ☐ |

     Criticism _____

     _____

   **b** Say why this is a good response to the same question.

| Mark on a scale from 1 (learnt a lot) to 5 (learnt little) |
| 1    2    3    4    5 |

     Reason _____

     _____

     _____

**9** There are 2000 students in a school.
To find out their views on vegetarianism some students do a survey. Melinda surveys 10 students picked at random from the school roll. Nandi surveys 30 students picked at random from the school roll. Owen surveys 100 students picked at random from the school roll.

Who will get the most reliable results? Give a reason for your answer.

_____

_____

**1** What is the probability of throwing a head with a coin? _____

*1 mark*

**2** An ordinary six-sided dice is thrown.
What is the probability that it lands on an even number? _____

*1 mark*

**3** Here are four events.

**A** Throwing a tail with a coin.

**B** Snow in June.

**C** Walking on Jupiter.

**D** High temperatures in Singapore all year round.

Mark each event on the following probability scale.

| Impossible | Very unlikely | Unlikely | Evens | Likely | Very likely | Certain |

0                          1

*2 marks*

**4** This bag contains 3 white balls and 7 blue balls.
A ball is taken from the bag at random.

**a** What is the probability it is blue?

_____

*1 mark*

**b** What is the probability it is white?

_____

*1 mark*

**5** The following cards are placed face down and shuffled.

S  T  A  T  I  S  T  I  C  S

A card is picked at random.

**a** What is the probability it is **not** a vowel? _____

*1 mark*

**b** What is the probability it is a **T**? _____

*1 mark*

**6** In a youth club, the probability that a member picked at random is a girl is $\frac{4}{7}$.
What is the probability that a member picked at random is a boy?

_____

*1 mark*

**7** A bag contains 1 blue ball and 4 red balls.

Some blue balls are to be added to the bag to make the chance of picking a blue ball at random $\frac{1}{2}$.

How many blue balls should be added? _____

**1 mark**

**8** A box of toffees contains a mix of nut and plain toffees.

The probability of getting a plain toffee is $\frac{9}{20}$.

What is the probability of getting a nut toffee?

_____

**1 mark**

**9** Here are four events.

**A** Throwing a three with a dice.

**B** Picking a vowel at random from the letters

D I S T R I B U T I O N

**C** The next person that comes into the room has a birthday in January.

**D** Throwing a number that is a factor of 24 with an ordinary dice.

Mark each event on the following probability scale.

```
|    |    |    |    |    |    |    |    |    |    |    |
0                           1                       1
                            2
```

**2 marks**

**10** This bag contains 4 white balls, 6 black balls and 5 striped balls.
A ball is taken from the bag at random.

**a** What is the probability it is black? _____

**1 mark**

**b** What is the probability it is not striped? _____

**1 mark**

# HANDLING DATA  Probability 2

**1** The following cards are placed face down and shuffled.

S  T  A  T  I  S  T  I  C  S

**a** A card is picked at random.

What is the probability it is **not** a letter S or a letter T?

_____

1 mark

**b** A card is picked at random. It is a vowel. **It is thrown away**.

Another card is picked at random.

What is the probability it is a letter **S or T**?

_____

1 mark

**2** In a church choir, the probability that a member picked at random is a woman is $\frac{14}{25}$.

What is the probability that a member picked at random is a man?

_____

1 mark

**3** A box contains 10 coloured balls.

A ball is taken out, its colour noted and then replaced.

This is repeated 1000 times.

The results are Red 822 times, Blue 178 times.

How many red balls and blue balls are in the box?

Red _____   Blue _____

2 marks

**4** The sample space diagram shows the outcomes from throwing two coins.

There are four outcomes altogether.

**a** What is the probability of throwing two heads with two coins?

_____

1 mark

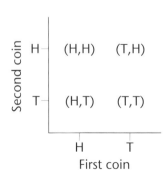

**b** What is the probability of throwing a head and a tail in any order with two coins?

_____

1 mark

**5** Three coins are thrown at once. The outcomes could be, for example, HHH, HHT, HTH.

  **a** What are all the possible outcomes?

_____

1 mark

  **b** What is the probability of three heads?

_____

1 mark

**6** The sample space diagram shows the outcomes for throwing two dice.

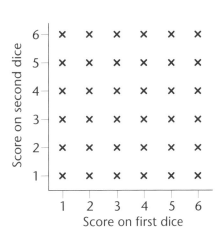

  **a** What is the probability of throwing a 'double', i.e. the same score on each dice?

_____

1 mark

  **b** What is the probability of a score of 4?

_____

1 mark

  **c** What is the probability of a score of 10 or over?

_____

1 mark

**7** This bag contains 4 white balls and 6 black balls.
A ball is taken from the bag at random and then replaced.
Another ball is then taken out.

  **a** What is the probability both balls were black?

_____

1 mark

  **b** What is the probability both balls were the same colour?

_____

1 mark

**8** A four-sided spinner is spun twice.

  **a** Complete the sample space diagram showing all the possible total scores.

1 mark

  **b** What is the probability of getting a score that is

    **i** even? _____

1 mark

    **ii** a square number? _____

1 mark

    **iii** a score above 5? _____

1 mark

First score

| | | 1 | 2 | 3 | 4 |
|---|---|---|---|---|---|
| Second score | 1 | 2 | | | |
| | 2 | | | | |
| | 3 | | | | |
| | 4 | | | | |

# Practice Paper 1

Time allowed 60 minutes.
You may **<u>not</u>** use a calculator on this paper.

1 The timetable shows the times of the number 32 and 32X bus from Greendale to Oxton.

| Stop | 32 | 32X |
|------|------|------|
| Greendale | 07:55 | 08:10 |
| Smithies | 08:03 | 08:18 |
| Horton | 08:20 | ↓ |
| Witton | 08:32 | ↓ |
| Oxton | 08:52 | 08:41 |

a What time does the 32 bus get to Smithies?

_____
*1 mark*

b How long does the 32X take to get from Greendale to Oxton?

_____
*1 mark*

c What do the arrows mean in the column for the 32X bus?

_____
*1 mark*

2 Fill in the missing numbers.

a  [ 52 ] + [ _____ ] = [ 100 ]

_____
*1 mark*

b  [ 25 ] × [ _____ ] = [ 100 ]

_____
*1 mark*

c  [ 600 ] ÷ [ _____ ] = [ 100 ]

_____
*1 mark*

d  [ 35 ] × [ 2 ] + [ _____ ] = [ 100 ]

_____
*1 mark*

**3** Look at the 3-D shapes.

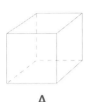
**A**

**B**

**C**

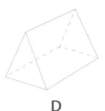
**D**

**a** One of the shapes is a triangular prism.
Write the letter of this shape.

*1 mark*

**b** How many edges has shape C?

*1 mark*

**c** How many vertices does shape A have?

*1 mark*

**4** The diagram shows a rectangle.
Its length is 4.2 cm and its width is 2.5 cm.

4.2 cm

2.5 cm

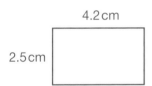

**a** Two of the rectangles are joined together in different ways to make two new rectangles.

The length of this rectangle is  cm.

*1 mark*

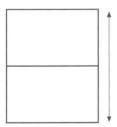

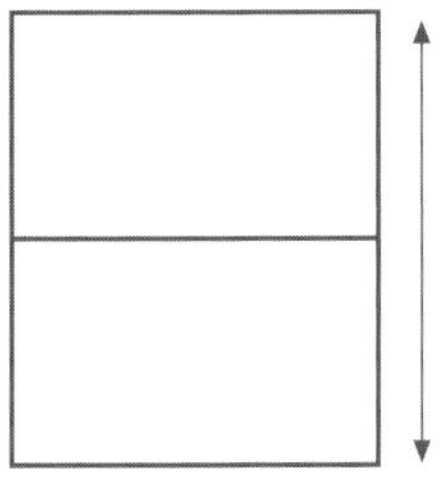

The width of this rectangle is  cm.

*1 mark*

**b** How many of the rectangles are needed to make a new rectangle
with a width of 15 cm?

*1 mark*

**5** Reflect each shape in the given mirror line.

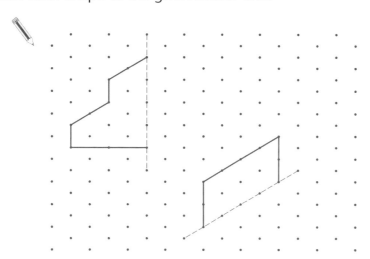

*2 marks*

**6** Brian buys a computer costing £1040.
He pays a deposit of £200.
He then pays the remainder in six equal instalments.
How much is each instalment?

£ _____

*2 marks*

**7** A litre bottle of lemonade is shared out equally
between five children.
Work out how much each child gets.
Give your answer in centilitres.

_____ cl

*1 mark*

**8** This quadrilateral has one acute angle and three obtuse angles.

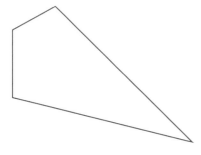

**a** Now draw a quadrilateral which has two acute angles and two obtuse angles.

*1 mark*

**b** Explain why you cannot draw a quadrilateral which has four acute angles.

_____

*1 mark*

**9** **a** Complete the following sentences.

_____ out of 200 is the same as 40%

*1 mark*

30 out of 50 is the same as _____ %

*1 mark*

**b** Complete the following sentence.

_____ out of _____ is the same as 5%

*1 mark*

**10** Anna buys a box of chocolates that are all the same size and shape. The box contains 12 milk chocolates, 8 plain chocolates and 5 white chocolates.
Anna takes a chocolate from the box at random.

**a** What is the probability that she takes a milk chocolate?

_____

*1 mark*

**b** What is the probability that she takes a plain chocolate?

_____

*1 mark*

**c** What is the probability that she does not take a white chocolate?

_____

*1 mark*

**11** A single ticket on the metro costs £1.35.
Dave buys a book of 25 single tickets, which costs him £30.
How much does Dave save by buying a book of tickets?

£_____

*2 marks*

**12** When $a = 6$, $b = 5$ and $c = 2$,

**a** work out the value of the following:

$a + 2b + c$

_____

*1 mark*

$3a + b - 2c$

_____

*1 mark*

**b** If $a + b + c + d = 20$, work out the value of $d$.

_____

*1 mark*

**13** Here is a fraction strip.

| $\frac{1}{2}$ | | |
|---|---|---|
| $\frac{1}{3}$ | | |
| $\frac{1}{4}$ | | | |
| $\frac{1}{12}$ | | | | | | | | | | | |

Use the fraction strip to help you work out the following:

$\frac{1}{2} + \frac{5}{12} =$ _____

_1 mark_

$\frac{1}{4} + \frac{1}{3} =$ _____

_1 mark_

$\frac{3}{4} - \frac{5}{12} =$ _____

_1 mark_

**14 a** Complete the table for the mapping $y = x + 5$.

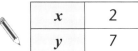

| $x$ | 2 | 4 | 6 |
|---|---|---|---|
| $y$ | 7 | | |

_1 mark_

**b** Complete the table for the mapping $y = 2x - 3$.

| $x$ | 2 | 4 | 6 |
|---|---|---|---|
| $y$ | 1 | | |

_1 mark_

**c** Write down the mapping for this table.

| $x$ | 2 | 4 | 6 |
|---|---|---|---|
| $y$ | 2 | 3 | 4 |

 $y =$ _____

_1 mark_

**15**

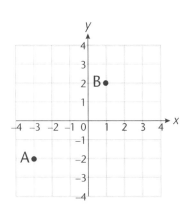

**a** What are the coordinates of the point A?

( _____ , _____ )

_1 mark_

**b** What are the coordinates of the mid-point of AB?

( _____ , _____ )

_1 mark_

**16** Here are three cuboids.

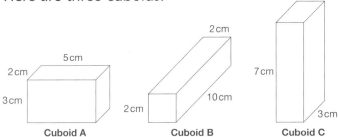

Cuboid A            Cuboid B            Cuboid C

**a** Which of the cuboids has the largest surface area?
Tick (✓) the correct box.

Cuboid A ☐     Cuboid B ☐     Cuboid C ☐

*2 marks*

**b** Which of the cuboids has the largest volume?
Tick (✓) the correct box.

Cuboid A ☐     Cuboid B ☐     Cuboid C ☐

*2 marks*

**c** Cuboid D has the same volume as Cuboid A.
Cuboid D has a length of 10 cm and width of 3 cm.
What is its height?

_____ cm

*1 mark*

**17** Three quadrilaterals are drawn on square grids below.

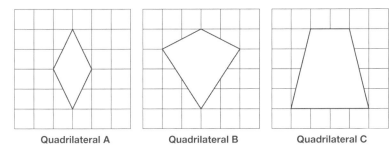

Quadrilateral A       Quadrilateral B       Quadrilateral C

**a** Is Quadrilateral A a square? Tick (✓) the correct box.   Yes ☐   No ☐
Explain your answer.

_____

*1 mark*

**b** Is Quadrilateral B a kite? Tick (✓) the correct box.   Yes ☐   No ☐
Explain your answer.

_____

*1 mark*

**c** Is Quadrilateral C a parallelogram? Tick (✓) the correct box.   Yes ☐   No ☐
Explain your answer.

_____

*1 mark*

**18** Fill in the missing numbers in the boxes.

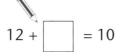

$12 +$ ☐ $= 10$

*1 mark*

$6 -$ ☐ $= 10$

*1 mark*

$-2 \times$ ☐ $= 10$

*1 mark*

**19** Work out $\frac{2}{3} \times \frac{3}{8}$

Write your answer as a fraction in its simplest form. _____

*2 marks*

**20** Solve the following equations.

$2x + 3 = 11$  $\qquad$  $x =$ _____

*1 mark*

$3(y - 2) = 9$  $\qquad$  $y =$ _____

*1 mark*

$3z - 4 = z + 2$  $\qquad$  $z =$ _____

*1 mark*

**21** 15 members of a slimming club record their weights before and after dieting for 3 months.
The stem-and-leaf diagrams show the weights before and after the diet.

| **Before** | 5 | | | | | | **After** | 5 | 4 | 4 | 6 | 9 | | **Key:** |
|---|---|---|---|---|---|---|---|---|---|---|---|---|---|---|
| | 6 | 5 | 7 | 9 | | | | 6 | 3 | 5 | 6 | 8 | 4 | 7\|2 means 72 kg |
| | 7 | 2 | 3 | 6 | 6 | 6 9 | | 7 | 1 | 2 | 2 | 2 | 9 | |
| | 8 | 0 | 2 | 4 | 8 | | | 8 | 3 | | | | | |
| | 9 | 2 | 5 | | | | | 9 | | | | | | |

Complete the following sentences.

**a** Before the diet the heaviest person was _____ kg and
_____ members of the club were over 70 kg.

*1 mark*

**b** After the diet the heaviest person was _____ kg and
_____ members of the club were over 70 kg.

*1 mark*

**c** Before the diet the modal weight was _____ kg and
the range of the weights was _____ kg.

*1 mark*

**22** Rearrange the following equations.

$x + y = 7$  $\qquad$  $x =$ _____

*1 mark*

$3w = z$  $\qquad$  $w =$ _____

*1 mark*

# Practice Paper 2

Time allowed 60 minutes.
You may use a calculator on this paper.

---

**1** A clothes shop displays the following items.

**a** Mr Jones buys an overcoat and a shirt.
How much does he pay altogether?

£ _____

*1 mark*

**b** Mrs Smith has £20. She buys two pairs of socks
for her husband. How much change does she get?

£ _____

*1 mark*

**c** Frank has £100. Does he have enough money
to buy a jacket, shoes and a shirt?

Yes ☐  No ☐

*1 mark*

**2** This table shows information about pupils in Class 8Q.

| Class 8Q | Right handed | Left handed |
|----------|--------------|-------------|
| Boys | 8 | 4 |
| Girls | 10 | 5 |

**a** How many pupils in 8Q are left handed? _____

*1 mark*

**b** Complete the bar chart to show the number of girls in 8Q.

*1 mark*

**c** This is the bar chart for Class 8P. In 8P a quarter of the
boys are left handed and one third of the girls are
left handed.
Fill in the missing numbers in the table below.

| Class 8P | Right handed | Left handed |
|----------|--------------|-------------|
| Boys | | |
| Girls | | |

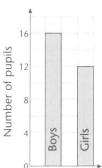

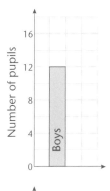

*2 marks*

**3** Here are some metric units.

| kilograms | grams | litres |

| centimetres | millimetres | centilitres |

Fill in the units from the list which best complete each sentence below.

To measure the **width** of a pencil I would use _____

*1 mark*

To measure the **mass** of a car I would use _____

*1 mark*

**4** Here is a shaded shape on a 1 cm grid.

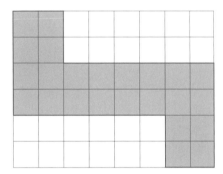

**a** What is the area of the shape? _____ cm²

*1 mark*

**b** The shape is the net of a cube.
What is the volume of the cube? _____

*2 marks*

**c** Now draw a rectangle that has the same area as the shaded shape.

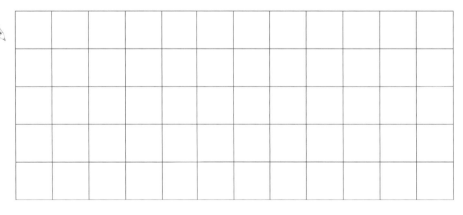

*1 mark*

**5 a** VAT in Britain is charged at $17\frac{1}{2}$ %.
A camera is priced as £280 excluding VAT.
What is $17\frac{1}{2}$ % of £280?

£ _____

*2 marks*

**b** In America, sales tax is charged on goods.
A camera costing $120 excluding sales tax had $6.00
sales tax added to the price. What percentage of 120 is 6? _____ %

*2 marks*

**6** Look at these shapes each made from two white cubes and one grey cube.

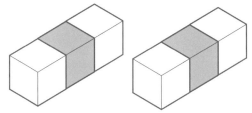

**a** The two shapes are put together to make a T-shape.
Shade in the faces that are grey.

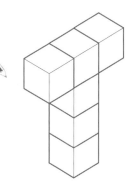

*1 mark*

**b** The two shapes are put together to make an L-shape.
Draw the L-shape on the grid below.

*2 marks*

**7** The pie chart shows the replies to a survey on holiday destinations.

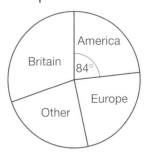

**a** 7 people answered 'America'.
How many people were in the survey altogether? _____ people

*2 marks*

**b** A different survey of 20 people were asked if they preferred staying
in Britain or going abroad for their holidays.
9 people said they preferred to stay in Britain.
On a pie chart, what would the angle be for 'Staying in Britain'?

_____ degrees

*2 marks*

**8 a** For each number in the table write a factor of that number that is between 10 and 20.

| Number | Factor between 10 and 20 |
|--------|--------------------------|
| 48     |                          |
| 150    |                          |
| 51     |                          |

*3 marks*

**b** Is 150 a multiple of 60? Tick (✓) Yes or No.

Yes ☐ No ☐

Explain how you know.

_____

*1 mark*

**9** The triangle $ABC$ below is drawn accurately.

**a** Measure accurately the angle marked $x$.  _____ degrees

*1 mark*

**b** The drawing is a scale drawing of a building plot.
The scale is **1 cm represents 50 metres**.
What is the actual length represented by $BC$ on the diagram?

_____ metres

*2 marks*

**10** Here are eight number cards.

-3  -1  -1  0  2  6  8  9

**a** What is the range of the numbers?  _____

*1 mark*

**b** What is the sum of the numbers?  _____

*1 mark*

**c** What is the mode of the numbers?  _____

*1 mark*

**d** What is the median of the numbers?  _____

*1 mark*

**e** What is the mean of the numbers?  _____

*2 marks*

**11** Here is part of a number grid.

| | | | | | |
|---|---|---|---|---|---|
| 23 | 24 | 25 | 26 | 27 | 28 |
| 33 | 34 | 35 | 36 | 37 | 38 |
| 43 | 44 | 45 | 46 | 47 | 48 |

From these numbers, write down one that is:

**a** a prime number ____________ *1 mark*

**b** a square number ____________ *1 mark*

**c** Explain why a square number could never be a prime number.

________________________________________ *1 mark*

**12 a** ABC is an isosceles triangle.

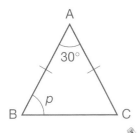

What is angle $p$? ____________ degrees

*1 mark*

**b** This diagram is not drawn accurately.
Calculate the size of angle $m$.
Show your working.

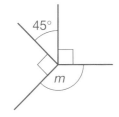

________________________ degrees *1 mark*

**13** A 50p coin has a mass of 8 grams.
How much is one kilogram of 50p coins worth?

£ ____________

*3 marks*

**14** The graph shows a straight line.

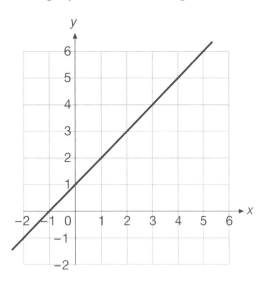

**a** Fill in the table with some of the points on the line.

| $(x, y)$ | ( __ , __ ) | ( __ , __ ) | ( __ , __ ) |
|---|---|---|---|

*2 marks*

**b** Write down the equation of the line. _____

*1 mark*

**c** On the graph draw the line $y = x + 3$

*1 mark*

**15** Use your calculator to work out

$(52 + 25) \times (41 - 19) =$ _____

*1 mark*

$\dfrac{52 + 25}{41 - 19} =$ _____

*1 mark*

**16** A bicycle wheel has a diameter of 70 cm.

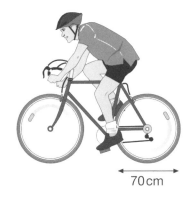

70 cm

**a** What is the circumference of the wheel?

_____ cm

*1 mark*

**b** During a 5 kilometre race, approximately how many times will the wheel turn?

_____ turns

*2 marks*

**17** The standard measure for different paper sizes are
A1, A2, A3 etc. ...
The standard measure for envelopes are C1, C2, C3 etc. ...
All paper and envelope sizes have the width and height
in the same ratio of approximately 1 : 1.4

Ratio of width to
height is 1 : 1.4

   a  Work out the height of a piece of A4 paper
that is 21 cm wide.

    A4 paper has a height of

    _____ cm

←—21 cm —→

A4

*1 mark*

   b  Work out the width of a C5 envelope that is
229 mm high.
Give your answer to the nearest millimetre.

    A C5 envelope has a width of

    _____ mm

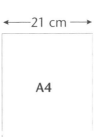

229 mm

C5

*1 mark*

   c  Will an A4 piece of paper, when folded in half, fit inside a C5 envelope?
Explain your answer.

_____

_____

*1 mark*

**18** Some information about the capacity of two football grounds is shown in the table.

|  | Manchester United | Manchester City |
| --- | --- | --- |
| **Total capacity** | 67 500 | 48 000 |
| **Percentage of executive seats** | 3.4% | 4.9% |

Which club has the most executive seats and by how many? _____

*2 marks*

**19** Look at this equation.

$3(2x + 13) = 76 + 4x$

Is $x = 18.5$ a solution of this equation? Tick [✓] Yes or No.

Yes ☐   No ☐

Explain your answer. _____

*1 mark*

# Mental Mathematics Test

In your mental mathematics test, you will hear the questions and write your answers on the answer sheets. For the first group of questions you will have 5 seconds to work out each answer and write it down.

**Time: 5 seconds**

**1** Multiply forty-three by ten.

| 1 | |
|---|---|

**2** How many metres are in 300 centimetres?

| 2 | | 300 cm |
|---|---|---|

**3** What is one-fifth of thirty-five?

| 3 | |
|---|---|

**4** Subtract four from minus six.

| 4 | | −6 |
|---|---|---|

**5** Look at the equation. When $x$ equals six, what is the value of $y$?

| 5 | | $y = x^2 - 5$ |
|---|---|---|

**6** What is four point five divided by two?

| 6 | | 4.5 |
|---|---|---|

**7** To the nearest ten kilometres the length of a motorway is ninety kilometres.

What is the least value the length of the motorway could be?

| 7 | km |
|---|---|

**For the next group of questions you will have 10 seconds to work out each answer and write it down.**

**Time: 10 seconds**

**8** The chart shows the number of hours of TV watched by a child in a week.

On which day was 3 hours of TV watched?

| 8 | 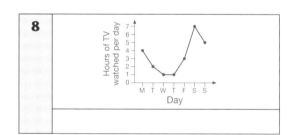 |
|---|---|

**9** A robot moves so that it is always the same distance from a fixed point.

What is the name of the shape of the robot's path?

| 9 | |
|---|---|

**10** Look at the grid. Write down the coordinates of the point B.

| 10 | 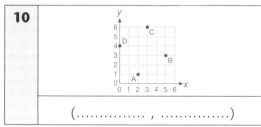 |
|---|---|

(............... , ...............)

**11** How many fifths are there in two?

| 11 | |
|---|---|

**12** Think about the mass two kilograms.

About how many pounds is that?

Circle the best answer on the answer sheet.

| 12 | 3    3.5    4    4.5    5 |
|---|---|

**13** Look at the fraction.

Write it in its simplest form.

| 13 | | $\dfrac{150}{200}$ |
|---|---|---|

**14** In a survey one-third of the people asked preferred to go abroad for their holidays.

What percentage is this?

| 14 | |
|---|---|

**15** What is the area of this rectangle?

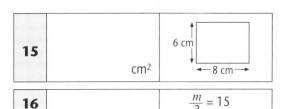

**16** Look at the equation. Solve it to find the value of *m*.

**17** The average weight of a male squirrel is 500 grams.

Female squirrels have an average weight that is 5% less than this.

What is the average weight of a female squirrel?

| 17 | g |
|----|----|

**18** A cardboard box measures half a metre by thirty centimetres by twenty centimetres.

Which of the calculations on the answer sheet will give the volume of the box?

Ring the correct answer.

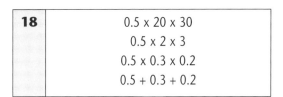

**19** What is a quarter of two thirds of sixty?

| 19 | |
|----|----|

**20** Look at the inequality.

How many integer solutions are there?

| 20 | $3 \leq n \leq 9$ |
|----|----|

**For the next group of questions you will have 15 seconds to work out each answer and write it down.**

**Time: 15 seconds**

**21** Write down a factor of 48 that is bigger than ten but less than twenty.

| 21 | |
|----|----|

**22** The first odd number is one. What is the hundredth odd number?

| 22 | |
|----|----|

**23** On the grid sketch the line $x + y = 4$.

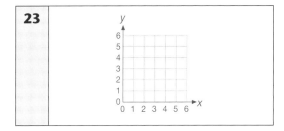

**24** What is the area of a circle with a radius of 3 centimetres?

Give your answer in terms of $\pi$.

| 24 | cm² |
|----|----|

**25** I can make twenty-four different four-digit numbers from the digits one, two, three and four.

How many of these will be odd numbers?

**26** Look at the calculation.

Write down an approximate answer.

| 26 | $\dfrac{38.5 \times 51.6}{4.89}$ |
|----|----|

**27** Complete the factorisation.

| 27 | $x^2 - 16 = (x + 4)\,(\text{.....................})$ |
|----|----|

**28** A bag contains only red and blue balls.

There are twice as many blue balls as red balls.

I take a ball at random from the bag.

What is the probability that the ball will be red?

| 28 | |
|----|----|

**29** What 3-D shape has four edges?

| 29 | |
|----|----|

**30** What is the sum of all the integers from 1 to 10?

1  2  3  4  5
6  7  8  9  10

# Revision checklist

## Number

I am able to:

- Recognise the value of a digit in a number ☐
- Apply the four rules to whole numbers and decimals ☐
- Add and subtract negative numbers ☐
- Cancel fractions ☐
- Find equivalent fractions, percentages and decimals ☐
- Find a percentage of a quantity ☐
- Find one quantity as a percentage of another ☐
- Cancel ratios ☐
- Divide a quantity in a given ratio ☐
- Add fractions with different denominators ☐
- Multiply and divide fractions ☐

## Algebra

I am able to:

- Give the next number in a number pattern and describe the pattern ☐
- Find multiples and factors of numbers ☐
- Recognise square numbers, triangular numbers and prime numbers ☐
- Simplify algebraic expressions ☐
- Use formulae expressed in words and in symbols ☐
- Find the $n$th term of a series ☐
- Give the coordinates of a point in any quadrant ☐
- Draw a graph by plotting points ☐
- Recognise graphs of the form $x = a$, $y = b$ and $y = x$ ☐
- Find the relationship between $x$ and $y$ values from the coordinates ☐
- Work out the value of calculations using the rules of BODMAS ☐
- Solve simple equations by rearrangement ☐
- Solve equations where the unknown appears on both sides of the equals sign ☐
- Solve equations using trial and improvement ☐

## Shape, Space and Measures

I am able to:

- Convert metric units and imperial units ☐
- Read scales accurately ☐
- Measure angles and bearings ☐
- Calculate angles from known facts ☐
- Recognise line and rotational symmetry ☐
- Recognise the standard triangles, quadrilaterals and other polygons ☐
- Calculate the interior and exterior angles of regular polygons ☐
- Reflect and rotate a shape ☐
- Enlarge a shape ☐
- Recognise the standard 3-D shapes and their nets ☐
- Calculate the perimeter and area of standard shapes ☐
- Calculate the circumference and area of a circle ☐
- Calculate the volume of cuboids ☐

## Handling Data

I am able to:

- Collect discrete and continuous data using frequency tables ☐
- Calculate the mean, mode, median and range ☐
- Compare distributions using an average and the range ☐
- Draw and interpret frequency diagrams from discrete and grouped tables ☐
- Draw and interpret line graphs ☐
- Draw and interpret pie charts ☐
- Draw and interpret scatter diagrams and lines of best fit ☐
- Design and criticise questions for surveys ☐
- Understand the likelihood of events ☐
- Mark events on a probability scale ☐
- Calculate the probability of an event ☐
- Calculate the probability of a combined event from a sample space diagram ☐